MW00784212

justinguitar.com
Rock Songbook

Published by
Wise Publications
14-15 Berners Street, London W1T 3LJ, UK.

Exclusive Distributors:
Music Sales Limited
Distribution Centre, Newmarket Road,
Bury St Edmunds, Suffolk IP33 3YB, UK.
Music Sales Corporation
180 Madison Avenue, 24th Floor,
New York NY 10016, USA.
Music Sales Pty Limited
Units 3-4, 17 Willfox Street, Condell Park
NSW 2200, Australia.

Order No. AM1005180
ISBN: 978-1-78038-687-4
This book © Copyright 2013 Wise Publications,
a division of Music Sales Limited.

Unauthorised reproduction of any part of this
publication by any means including photocopying
is an infringement of copyright.

Written, compiled and arranged by Justin Sandercoe.
Edited by Toby Knowles.
Design by Fresh Lemon.
Cover design by Paul Agar.
Cover photographs by Nick Delaney.
With thanks to Dario Cortese.
Printed in the EU.

justinguitar.com
Rock Songbook

Wise Publications
part of The Music Sales Group
London / New York / Paris / Sydney / Copenhagen / Berlin / Madrid / Hong Kong / Tokyo

Your Guarantee of Quality
As publishers, we strive to produce every
book to the highest commercial standards.
This book has been carefully designed to
minimise awkward page turns and to make
playing from it a real pleasure.
Particular care has been given to specifying
acid-free, neutral-sized paper made from pulps
which have not been elemental chlorine bleached.
This pulp is from farmed sustainable forests and was
produced with special regard for the environment.
Throughout, the printing and binding have been
planned to ensure a sturdy, attractive publication
which should give years of enjoyment.
If your copy fails to meet our high standards,
please inform us and we will gladly replace it.

www.musicsales.com

www.justinguitar.com

Contents

INTRODUCTION

 Welcome to my Rock Songbook!

This book is for guitar players who have worked through the basics of playing, and are now aiming to progress beyond beginner level. I've had a great time working on this book and I'm sure you will have a great time playing these classic rock songs. I expect many of you will have completed my free online Beginner's Guitar Course and perhaps learned songs from the *Justinguitar.com Beginner's Songbook*. This book continues on from there and introduces material used in the Intermediate Method (also free on the website), including barre chords and sixteenth-note strumming.

There are four sections to the book, starting with a 'Beginner' section, and ending with a section of full TAB transcriptions. The Beginner section mainly uses chords, rhythms and techniques covered in my Beginner's Guitar Course, with a few new tricks thrown in to keep things interesting. It's a great selection of tunes, which are fun to play, not too tricky to master, and which will help you consolidate your knowledge.

The 'Intermediate' section introduces barre chords. Playing barre chords is probably the most important skill to learn, after you've become confident with all your beginner techniques. Some songs use only barre chords, while others mix them with open chords—you'll need to master both approaches. If you are uncertain about how to play barre chords, please check out the relevant lessons on the website.

Next up we have 'Intermediate Plus' which, as the name suggests, uses many of the skills and techniques covered in the Intermediate Method but adds some other interesting elements, such as new chords, more complex rhythm patterns and riffs.

Lastly, we have five full guitar TAB transcriptions, which should prove a little more challenging and give you something to work towards! These songs feature quite a few different techniques, and they're all rock classics.

Some of you are bound to wonder why a few well-known artists have been omitted from the book—there are no songs by Red Hot Chili Peppers, Metallica or Green Day, for example. In short, it's about who owns the sheet music publishing rights—some acts are signed to publishers that won't allow their songs to appear in 'mixed folio' publications (songbooks that feature a variety of different artists—like this one) and others want to keep the songs for their own books, so won't allow my publisher permission for us to use them in this book.

I'd like to thank Toby and Tom at Music Sales for their help and suggestions, and also the many users that offered song suggestions. Thanks also to Jed Wardley for helping get this book to you, Dario Cortese for proofreading and helping with transcriptions and to the forum moderators (Tom, Lieven, Jonathan and Richard) for their massive contribution to our community.

If you enjoy this book then you might like to keep an eye out for others in this series, which includes a range of styles including acoustic, pop and vintage. I hope you enjoy playing the songs in this book and wish you a lot of joy on your musical journey.

Justin Sandercoe
June 2013, London

If you get stuck with anything in this songbook then your first port of call should be my website where there are many hundreds of completely free lessons that will take you from complete novice level to wherever you want to go!

www.justinguitar.com

If you enjoy online interaction there is a great forum where there are many thousands of students helping each other every day! It really is a passionate, supportive and active community, and you are welcome to join it.

www.justinguitarcommunity.com

 Top 10 Practice Tips

1. Practise what you can't do, not what you can.

2. Practice makes permanent (not perfect). So get it right!

3. Start slowly and get it right before you speed up.

4. Using a timer saves time.

5. Focus on one element of a song at a time.

6. Try to practise a little every day, rather than a lot all on one day.

7. Keep track of your practice: use a practice schedule.

8. If it sounds good, it is good!

9. Playing and Practising are very different—don't confuse them.

10. The more you think, the more you stink! Practise until the part becomes instinctive.

Using Software

I would strongly suggest getting some software that will allow you to change the speed of a recording but not the pitch. I use one called *Transcribe!* but there are many others available, including *Audacity*, *Capo* and the *Amazing Slow Downer*.

Set the software to play the song at 50%, or at whatever speed you can practise in time with. Play along with the recording; use the 'cycle' feature to repeat one section (or the whole song) over and over. Once you are confident that you can play this section precisely, speed the track up, a little bit at a time. This may happen over the course of a few weeks, or in one practice session, depending on your ability and on the difficulty of the song.

Take time to learn how to use the software, in particular how to use the key commands (keyboard shortcuts). This will save you countless hours!

⌘ Practising Harder Material

When approaching a more complex song, start by having a mess around—play through the song a few times as well as you can, working out where the tricky bits are, and which sections will require the most attention. Pick one section and play it very slowly and accurately—I usually start with the main riff or theme, or perhaps the introduction. Make sure that you get it right. Every time you play something wrong you are entering 'bad code' into your brain.

Try to play this section with the correct rhythm, even if it is very slow. I recommend that you count out the beats while you're practising, as this will help a lot. Don't worry about the groove just yet, but concentrate on precision, making sure that your timing is mathematically correct.

Try to get this first 'chunk' into your memory as soon as you can. Your goal should be to play while looking at your guitar (or closing your eyes), rather than following the music on the page. After you have memorised this first 'chunk', you should build upon it. Learn the next section, slowly and carefully, and once you can play this new section in time (no matter how slowly), join it on to the first section. Work on creating a flow between the two sections, and practise both sections 'joined-up' until you can play them at 70-80% of the actual speed of the song.

Continue this process until you can play through the whole song at a slower tempo, and then start to speed the tempo up, until you can play at full speed. It's much better to play correctly at a slower tempo than to play at full speed, with mistakes. If there are one or two extra hard bits, extract them and work on them on their own. When they are sounding good enough, put them back into the whole song.

BEGINNER STAGE

 ## Introduction

This first chapter mainly uses the chords, rhythms and techniques covered in my Beginner's Course. The layout is the same as in my *Beginner's Songbook*, with chords and lyrics on one page and tips and rhythms on the facing page.

 ## Chords

For the most part, the chords used in this section are the eight essential open chords:

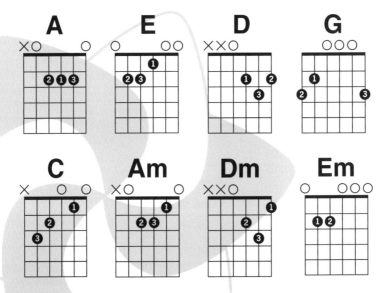

You'll also find a few variations of these and some basic slash chords.

 ## F Chord

I assume that you are also familiar with the F chord. Below left is the full barre version of the chord, and on the right is the smaller, simpler version of the chord.

Beginner

Intermediate

Intermediate +

TAB

 ## 7th Chords

We'll also be using these (dominant) 7th chords, which are also open chords, as shown below.

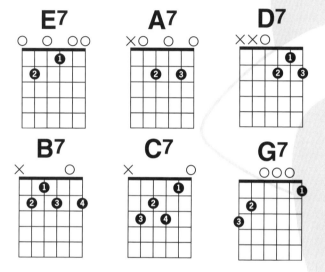

 ## Sus Chords

Lastly, we'll be playing a few sus chords, which again are nice, friendly open chords.

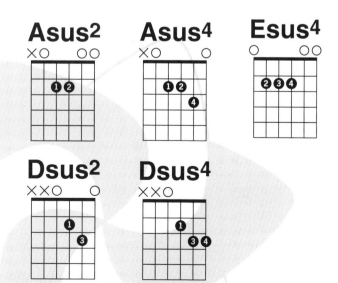

13

Highway To Hell

Words & Music by Angus Young, Malcolm Young & Bon Scott

Intro

riff ────────────────────

A ‖: N.C.   D/F♯ G5 | N.C.   D/F♯ G5 |

| D/F♯ G5   D/F♯ A | A N.C.   A :‖

Verse 1

with riff
Livin' easy, livin' free,
Season ticket on a one way ride.
Askin' nothin', leave me be,
Takin' ev'rythin' in my stride.
Don't need reason, don't need rhyme,
Ain't nothin' I'd rather do.
Goin' down, party time,

| D/F♯ G5   D/F♯ E5 | E5   (E5)
　　My friends are gonna be there too.

Chorus 1

E5   A | D/A G5 D/F♯ | A | D/A
　I'm on the highway to Hell,   On the highway to Hell.
| G5   D/F♯ | A | D/A
　　　Highway to Hell,
| G5   D/F♯ | A | D/A | D/A   A |
　I'm on the highway to Hell.

Verse 2

No stop signs, speed limit,
Nobody's gonna slow me down.
Like a wheel, gonna spin it,
Nobody's gonna mess me around.
Hey Satan, pay'n' my dues,
Playin' in a rockin' band.
Hey, Momma, look at me,
I'm on my way to the promised land.

Chorus 2

I'm on the highway to Hell, highway to Hell,
I'm on the highway to Hell,

| G5   D/F♯ | A | D/A | D/A Dsus4/A D/A |
　　　　　Highway to Hell.

D/A | D/A Dsus4/A D/A | D/A Dsus4/A D/A |
Don't stop me!

Guitar solo

‖: A   D/A | D/A   G5 D/F♯ :‖ (Play x4)

Chorus 3

As Chorus 1 (Play x2)

　　　　　　　　　　　　　　　A
And I'm goin' down all the way,　on the highway to Hell.

© COPYRIGHT 1979 J. ALBERT & SON PTY. LIMITED.
ALL RIGHTS RESERVED. INTERNATIONAL COPYRIGHT SECURED.

Beginner

Intermediate

Intermediate +

TAB

 # Introduction

AC/DC released this hard rock anthem in 1979—and it's been a rite of passage for rock guitarists ever since! If you're playing along with the recording, be aware that the song is tuned a little bit flat.

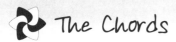

The Chords

This song uses mostly open chords, but the grips that Angus Young uses are quite specific and differ slightly from the traditional way of playing the chords—they are well worth looking at as they are used by many rock guitarists today.

Play the A chord with a first finger barre, making sure that the thinnest string is muted by lifting your 1st finger a little over that string. The D/F# is a common grip—some people prefer to play the bass note by reaching over with the thumb but I'm fairly sure Angus Young plays it with the fingers 1, 2 and 3 as shown below.

The G5 chord uses just two fingers, but as well as holding down notes they are both on muting duty too. The underside of the 2nd finger must mute the fifth string and your 3rd finger must mute the thinnest string as we don't want to hear this note for most of the song.

Just before the chorus we have a power chord on E, written as E5. For the chorus we add in just one more chord—the D/A which is the same as a regular D chord except that we deliberately play the open A string.

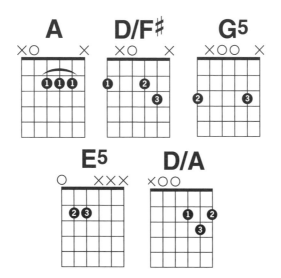

continued...

Beginner

Intermediate

Intermediate +

TAB

The Riff

The rhythm of this riff is just as important as the chords, so the riff is written out for you below showing the count, although you really must listen to these songs and get the rhythms in your head. You will be using all down-strums for this riff.

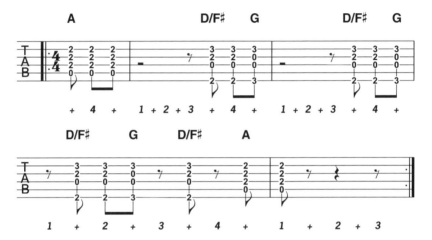

The Chorus

In the chorus, make sure you notice that the D/A is pushed (it changes on the 'and' after 4, and that the G5 to D/F♯ are on beats 3 and 4 respectively. You'll notice that I've tabbed out a 'full' D/F♯ chord—what we hear on the recording may well be a composite of Malcolm and Angus Young's guitars playing together. I've written it for just one guitar, which is more challenging to play, and may involve you having to get your thumb over for the bottom F♯! Note that the two open bass strings in bar 2 (below) are unlikely to have been hit deliberately, but they are certainly in there and leaving them out doesn't sound right! They are played quieter than the rest of the notes though.

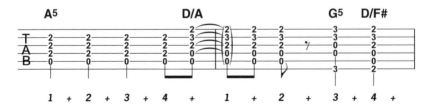

Every Rose Has Its Thorn

Words & Music by Bret Michaels, Bruce Johannesson,
Robert Kuykendall & Richard Ream

 ## Introduction

I still remember buying this song on vinyl from a record store and being completely confused by the gender of the band, Poison. The ambiguity sure didn't stop them having a Christmas No. 1 with this 'hair metal' ballad, back in 1988. Note that if you are playing along with the original recording, you'll need to tune your guitar down a semitone (use your tuner: E♭, A♭, D♭, G♭, B♭, E♭).

 ## Playing The Chords

This song confirmed to me and other kids my age (back in the 1980s) that to play in a rock band you had to use all four fingers to play G. These four-fingered G and Cadd9 chords seemed to feature in many songs from this era, and really contributed to the sound of the 80s rock ballad. Changing between them is a lot easier than regular G to C!

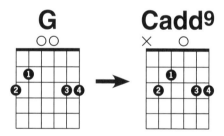

You'll also hear some sus4 additions to the D chords in the verse. I haven't included these Dsus4 chords in the chord chart as they appear only briefly, but listen out and see if you can slip them into your playing.

17

Every Rose Has Its Thorn

Words & Music by Bret Michaels, Bruce Johannesson,
Robert Kuykendall & Richard Ream

Beginner

Intermediate

Intermediate +

TAB

Intro

| G | Cadd⁹ | G | Cadd⁹ |

Verse 1

G   Cadd⁹
  We both lie silently still in the dead of the night,
          G   Cadd⁹
Although we both lie close together we feel miles apart inside.
     | G   Cadd⁹
Was it something I said or something I did,
     | G   Cadd⁹
Did my words not come out right?
     | D
Though I tried not to hurt you,
          C
Though I tried, but I guess that's why they say.

Chorus 1

G   Cadd⁹   G   Cadd⁹
Every rose has its thorn, just like every night has its dawn.
     | G   D |Cadd⁹   G |
Just like every cowboy sings his sad, sad song,
G   Cadd⁹
Every rose has its thorn, yeah it does.

Link 1

| G | Cadd⁹ | G | Cadd⁹ |

Verse 2

I listen to her favourite song playing on the radio,
Hear the DJ say love's a game of easy come and easy go.
But I wonder does he know,
Has he ever felt like this?
And I know that you'd be here right now
If I could let you know somehow. I guess...

Chorus 2

As Chorus 1

Bridge

|Em   D | C   G |
  Though it's been a while now, I can still feel so much pain
|Em   D |
  Like a knife that cuts you the wound heals,
C   (G)
  But the scar, that scar will remain.

Solo

| G | Cadd⁹ | G | Cadd⁹ |
| Em D | Cadd⁹ G | Em D | Cadd⁹ |

Link 2

| G | Cadd⁹ | G | Cadd⁹ |

Verse 3

I know I could of saved our love that night if I'd known what to say.
Instead of making love we both made our separate ways.

© COPYRIGHT 1988 WILLESDEN MUSIC INC.
IMAGEM MUSIC.
ALL RIGHTS RESERVED. INTERNATIONAL COPYRIGHT SECURED

(cont.)   And now I hear you found somebody new,
And that I never meant that much to you.
To hear that tears me up inside,
And to see you cuts me like a knife. I guess...

Chorus 3   As Chorus 1   *(Repeat to fade)*

 Layers

On the recording there are several different layers of guitar, which is
very typical of this style, including the obligatory 'clean' electric guitar
with chorus effect that joins in the second chorus, playing the same
chords as the acoustic guitar but picking out notes one at a time. The
trick with this kind of minimal guitar part is not to play too much, and
to focus on playing just a few notes and letting them ring out together.

 Rhythm

The strumming in this song is not very consistent so you have some
freedom to experiment a bit. However, you should ensure that you
keep your strumming hand moving consistently so that you stay in the
groove. You'll also find that the acoustic guitar part on the recording fits
really well around the melody. You must remember that as a rhythm
guitarist you are there to support the melody—bear that in mind and try
to listen to both what you play and the melody itself.

Below is the pattern played for most of the intro and first verse, which
is a good place to start.

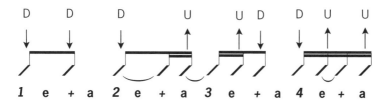

If You Tolerate This Your Children Will Be Next

Words by Nicky Wire; Music by James Dean Bradfield & Sean Moore

Intro

‖: Am | Em | F | C   G/B :‖

Verse 1

```
Am                        Em            F                 C
   The future teaches you to be alone, the present to be afraid and cold.
 F              C              G      G
So if I can shoot rabbits, then I can shoot fascists.
Am              Em             F              C
   Bullets for your brain today, but we'll forget it all a - gain.
                F
Monuments put from pen to paper
C                      G      G
Turns me into a gutless wonder.
```

Chorus 1

```
             Dm        Am                    G     G
And if you tolerate this then your children will be next.
             Dm        Am                  G
And if you tolerate this then your children will be next,
                 G
Will be next, will be next, will be next.
```

Link 1

| Am | Em | F | C   G/B |

Verse 2

Gravity keeps my head down, or is it maybe shame
At being so young and being so vain.
Holes in your head today, but I'm a pacifist.
I've walked La Ramblas but not with real intent.

Chorus 2

As Chorus 1

Instr.

| F | C | G | G |
| Dm | Am | G | G |

Bridge

```
           F              C          G      G
And on the street to - night an old man plays
            Dm     Am                 G      G
With newspaper cuttings of his glory days.
```

Chorus 3

As Chorus 1

Outro

‖: F | C | G | G | *(with Vocals 'Aah')*

| Dm | Am | G | G   :‖ *(Play x3)*

| F | C | G |

© COPYRIGHT 1998 SONY/ATV MUSIC PUBLISHING.
ALL RIGHTS RESERVED. INTERNATIONAL COPYRIGHT SECURED.

Introduction

A song with an important message, Manic Street Preachers released this track as a single, and later on their album, *This Is My Truth Tell Me Yours,* in 1998.

Playing The Chords

There are a couple of interesting instrumental parts running through this song: an acoustic guitar which is mainy strummed and a heavily effected keyboard part. The sound of the verse chords (with the 'pheeow' sound!) can be achieved on an electric guitar using delay and flanger/phaser effects. You can play the chords using basic open grips, strummed once and left to ring out (lengthened by the delay effect), though there is some more active playing in the chorus. Layering guitar parts is a very common rock technique and great fun to recreate if you are doing some home recording—start by recording the acoustic part and then add the layer of electric on top. You can also recreate these different layers if you are in a twin-guitar band or have a jam buddy.

The solo is not shown here but it's not hard—in fact it's a good one to try and work out on your own if you are getting into transcribing.

Rhythm

The acoustic guitar part is mostly strummed but you can clearly hear a few notes picked out during the intro for the change from C to G/B, as the acoustic part starts. Below is a guide strumming pattern, which changes with the dynamics of the song, so you need to follow these dynamic (volume) changes throughout the song.

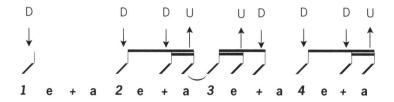

La Grange

Words & Music by Billy Gibbons, Dusty Hill & Frank Beard

Beginner

Intermediate

Intermediate +

TAB

Intro   Play **riff 1**

riff 2 (x8)

Verse 1   Rumour spreadin' a - round in that Texas town,
About that shack outside La Grange.
And you know what I'm talkin' about,
Just let me know if you wanna go.
To that home out on the range,
They gotta lotta nice girls, oh.

riff 2 (x4)

Link 1   Have mercy,
A haw, haw, haw, haw.
A haw, a haw, haw, haw.

riff 2 (x8)

Verse 2   Well, I hear it's fine if you've got the time,
And that ten to get yourself in ahmm, hmm,
And I hear it's tight most every night,
But now I might be mistaken.

Bridge   ‖: **C5** | **C5 E♭5 F5** | **C5** | **C5 E♭5 F5** :‖ *Play x8*

Play **riff 3 (x2)**

Link 2   Play **riff 1**

Outro   Play **riff 2**   *(Repeat to fade)*

© COPYRIGHT 1989 STAGE THREE MUSIC (CATALOGUES) LTD/MUSIC OF STAGE THREE
ADMINISTERED BY STAGE THREE MUSIC PUBLISHING LTD.
ALL RIGHTS RESERVED. INTERNATIONAL COPYRIGHT SECURED.

Introduction

ZZ Top, the beardy kings of Southern rock, released this bluesy single in 1973. It's a real masterclass on groove and awesome riffing!

The Riffs

Any of you who are familiar with the 12-Bar Blues Variations lesson in my Beginner's Course will recognise some of the finger positions and the concept of the main riffs here, which are rock riffs born out of the blues! If you want to 'change it up' a bit you might like to experiment with some of the other riffs covered in that lesson.

The main riff is played with many variations through the song—there are far too many to write out, but below are two of the most common ways that the riff is played, so start off with these and experiment and listen and see if you can find some others. Billy Gibbons plays these riffs fingerstyle, which you'll need to do too if you're after the authentic sound.

Riff 1

Intro: *Play x2*
Link 2: *Play x3*

Riff 2

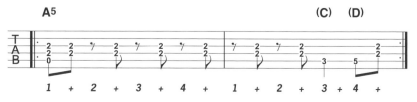

23

Bridge

The bridge rhythm guitar moves to the key of C and chugs along under a classic Billy Gibbons solo. At the end there is a tasty twin guitar riff taking us back to the breakdown, before even more solos! What legends!

 ## Bridge (cont.)

Riff 3

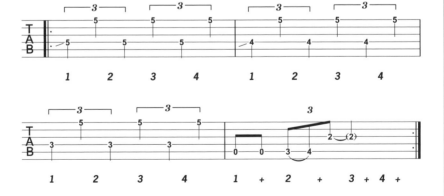

In Bloom
Words & Music by Kurt Cobain

Introduction

This song from Nirvana's grunge masterpiece, *Nevermind,* was a hit single for the band in 1992. The song follows the typical Nirvava structure of mellow verses, huge choruses and a really out-there guitar solo!

Intro

The most important thing here is making sure you get the rhythm really tight—you'll pick up the rhythm by listening to the track for sure, but I've written it out for you too. Make sure you don't let any of the open strings ring out, or it'll sound really ugly!

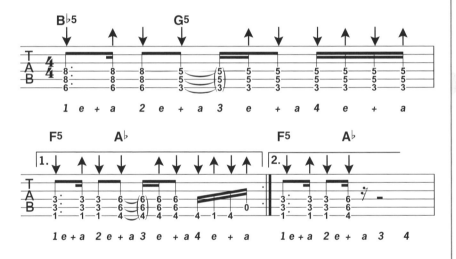

Verse

The verse chords are played with very heavy distortion until the vocals enter, and are then played with the classic 'clean with chorus' sound in the verses after a little break.

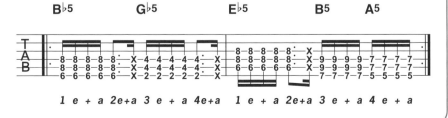

25

In Bloom

Words & Music by Kurt Cobain

Intro

‖: B♭5   G5   F5   A♭5 :‖

‖: B♭5   G♭5 | E♭5   B5 A5 :‖

Verse 1

| B♭5   G♭5 | E♭5 B5 A5 |
Sell the kids for food,
| B♭5   G♭5 | E♭5   B5 A5 |
Weather changes moods.
| B♭5   G♭5 | E♭5 B5 A5 |
Spring is here a - gain,
| B♭5   G♭5 | E♭5   B5 A5 |
Repro - ductive glands.

Chorus 1

| B♭5   G5 | B♭5   G5
He's the one who likes all our pretty songs,
   | B♭5   G5 | B♭5   G5
And he likes to sing a - long and he likes to shoot his gun.
     | C5   E♭ | C5   E♭
But he knows not what it means, knows not what it means.
      | B♭5   G5 | B♭5   G5
And I say he's the one who likes all our pretty songs,
   | B♭5   G5 | B♭5   G5
And he likes to sing a - long and he likes to shoot his gun.
     | C5   E♭ | C5   E♭
But he knows not what it means, knows not what it means.
     | (B♭5)
And I say yeah.

Link 1

‖: B♭5 | G5 | F5 | A♭5 :‖

Verse 2

We can have some more,
Nature is a whore.
Bruises on the fruit,
Tender age in bloom.

Chorus 2

As Chorus 1

Link 2

As Link 1

Instr.

‖: B♭5 | G♭5 | E♭5 | B5 A5 :‖ *Play x4*

Chorus 3

As Chorus 1

© COPYRIGHT 1992 THE END OF MUSIC/PRIMARY WAVE TUNES.
EMI VIRGIN MUSIC LTD.
ALL RIGHTS RESERVED. INTERNATIONAL COPYRIGHT SECURED.

...knows not what it means, knows not what it means.
And I say yeah.

Outro ‖: Bᵇ5 | G5 | F5 | Aᵇ5 :‖ Bᵇ5 |

 Chorus

The guitar parts are pretty simple here—rather than using a set strumming pattern, just thrash out the rhythm and give it loads of energy, because that's what the song needs. That said, you need to start somewhere, so I would begin with even eighth-note down-strums (four down-strums on each chord) and then add in some up-strums if it feels right; however the recording mainly uses heavy, eighth-note down-strums.

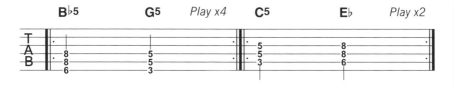

 Sounds

Getting the right guitar sounds for certain songs can be half the battle! For the verses you will need a smooth, clean electric sound to which you should add a chorus effect (most likely with the aid of stomp box) and experiment with the knobs to find the right settings (the different brands have such wide variables in settings that I can't really give you any exact settings. For the other sections of the song you need a big fat gnarly distortion sound—again you'll have to experiment with your stomp box to find the right settings, but the gain will have to be up pretty high for sure!

Rock And Roll All Nite

Words & Music by Paul Stanley & Gene Simmons

Beginner

Intermediate

Intermediate +

TAB

Intro

D riff

| A5 | E5 | A5 | E5 |

Verse 1

A5   E5
You show us every - thing you've got,

A5   E5
You keep on dancing and the room gets hot,

D5   E5   D riff
You drive us wild, we'll drive you cra - zy.

A5   E5
You say you wanna go for a spin,

A5   E5
The party's just begun, we'll let you in,

D5   E5   D riff
You drive us wild, we'll drive you cra - zy.

Pre-chorus 1

F5   G5   N.C.
You keep on shouting, you keep on shouting.

Chorus 1

A5   D5   E5
I wanna rock and roll all nite   and party every day.

A5   D5   E5
I wanna rock and roll all nite   and party every day.

A5   N.C.
I wanna rock and roll all nite and party every day.

                                                        D riff
I wanna rock and roll all nite and party every day.

Verse 2

You keep on saying you'll be mine for a while,
You're looking fancy and I like your style,
You drive us wild, we'll drive you crazy.
You show us everything you've got,
Baby, baby that's quite a lot,
And you drive us wild, we'll drive you crazy.

Pre-chorus 2 As Pre-chorus 1

Chorus 2

A5   D5   E5
I wanna rock and roll all nite   and party every day.

A5   D5   E5
I wanna rock and roll all nite   and party every day.

A5   N.C.
I wanna rock and roll all nite and party every day.
I wanna rock and roll all nite and party every day.

Chorus 3

A5   D5   E5
I wanna rock and roll all nite and party every day. *(Repeat to Fade)*

© COPYRIGHT 1975 HORI PRODUCTIONS AMERICA INCORPORATED/CAFE AMERICANA.
UNIVERSAL MUSIC PUBLISHING LIMITED.
ALL RIGHTS RESERVED. INTERNATIONAL COPYRIGHT SECURED.

Beginner

Intermediate

Intermediate +

TAB

 ## Introduction

Here's some proper anthemic rock 'n' roll from glam legends Kiss. The song featured on their album *Dressed To Kill* (1975).

Chord And Tuning Options

Interestingly, this song borrows heavily from blues rockers like the Rolling Stones. There are multiple guitar parts on the recording and I'm sure I can hear one of them in open-G tuning, although all guitars are tuned down one semitone (E^b Tuning). All of the chords can be played either as power chords or open chords (except the F, of course) or with the open-G Tuning.

In open position you can play just regular open chords, and you might like to incorpoate the '12 Bar Blues Shuffle' groove taught in my Beginner's Course. Using power chords (or major barre chords) you can add sus4 chords on beats 2 and 3 of the second bar of the rhythm pattern shown on the next page—this will which sound a lot like the open-tuning riff part but without the hassle of re-tuning. Make sure you lift off the sus for the 'and' after beat 3 for the proper effect!

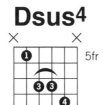

Dsus4

D Riff

The D Riff at the end of the verses is played with open tuning but here it is written out in normal tuning, as I imagine most of you will play it that way!

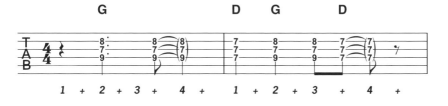

Beginner

Intermediate

Intermediate +

TAB

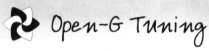

Open-G Tuning

If you want to try out the open-G Tuning, first tune your guitar down a semitone (as the whole song is effectively 'tuned down'), then drop both E strings and the A string down a tone. With the semitone drop you should now have D♭, G♭, D♭, G♭, B♭, D♭. In this tuning a regular major chord is just a simple barre on the thinnest 5 strings (you won't play the thickest string at all now).

The chords and the riff for each chord are shown below. This open-G riff was made popular by The Rolling Stones and is a standard riff for many rock bands.

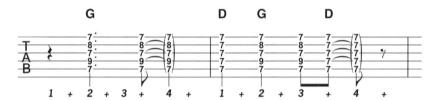

Open Tuning Chords

Open Tuning Riff (on A)

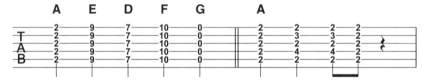

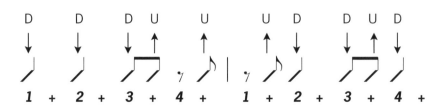

Rhythm

There are many possibilities for strumming but a good starting point is shown below. Remember that you can add your sus chord on beats 2 and 3 of the second bar.

There She Goes
Words & Music by Lee Mavers

Introduction

Liverpool's The La's only lasted for one album but turned out this classic song with a great 'jangly' riff, played on an electric 12-string guitar.

The Riff

There are a few layers of guitar in the track, the most obvious (and well-known) being the main riff shown below. There are a number of fingering options but I'd recommend putting your 2nd finger on the 3rd fret of string 2, and leaving it there for the whole riff. This will require a bit of stretching to reach the 5th fret with your pinky. If you can't crack that, experiment and see what works for you. Make sure you let the notes ring out together—it's a big part of the sound. The original is tracked with multiple guitars so don't be upset if you struggle to get your guitar sounding as big as the recording!

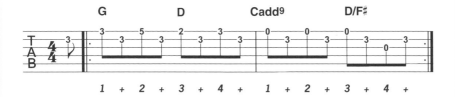

Towards the end of the intro, where the chord changes to Am, we have a new, albeit similar lick played over the chords. This lick appears again in the verses, in a slight variation:

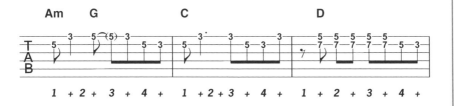

31

There She Goes

Words & Music by Lee Mavers

Intro

riff ─────────
‖: G   D | Cadd9   D/F♯ :‖   *(Play x6)*

riff (x1)
| G   D | Cadd9   G/B |

| Am   G | C | D |

Verse 1
(riff x3)

| G   D | Cadd9 D/F♯ |
There she goes,
| G   D | Cadd9   D/F♯ |
There she goes again
| G   D | Cadd9   G/B
Racing through my   brain,
    | Am   G | C
And I just can't con - tain
    | Am   G | C   D
This feeling that re - mains.

Verse 2

There she blows, there she blows again,
Pulsing through my vein,
And I just can't contain this feeling that remains.

Verse 3

Instrumental

Bridge

Em   C   Em | C
There she goes, there she goes a - gain:
      D | G   D | Cmaj7
She calls my name, pulls my train,
D | G   D | Cmaj7
No-one else could heal my pain.
    Am   Em   C   D
But I just can't con - tain, this feeling that re - mains.

Verse 4

There she goes, there she goes again,
Chasing down my lane,
And I just can't contain this feeling that remains.

Coda

(riff x3)
There she goes,
There she goes,   G
There she goes a - gain.

© COPYRIGHT 1988 GO! DISCS MUSIC.
UNIVERSAL/ISLAND MUSIC LIMITED.
ALL RIGHTS RESERVED. INTERNATIONAL COPYRIGHT SECURED.

 Strumming

The main acoustic guitar part plays the pattern shown below for most of the song but does pick up on some of the accents and variations as it goes along, so you need to listen out for them too—the most obvious is the 'lead in' where the acoustic comes in at the start of the track (at 0:15) which is played UDU, starting on the 'and' after beat 3, and the longer version which comes in on the 'and' after 1, which you can hear at 0:33.

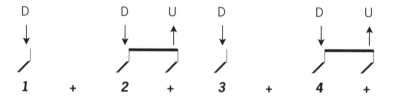

 Layers

There are a number of other layers: in the verses there is the acoustic guitar strumming along, an electric guitar which continues the riff, another electric rhythm guitar picking out notes one at a time and doing some light strumming accents, and at least one other acoustic (maybe a 12-string) alongside a few other incidental bits that drop in from time to time. Try to hear the parts and if you are getting into doing some home recording then have a go at creating some layers on your own— it's loads of fun and very rewarding!

Self Esteem

Words & Music by Bryan Holland

Beginner

Intermediate

Intermediate +

TAB

Intro

A5 F5	C5 G5	A5 F5	C5 G5
F5	F5 C5/G
A5 F5	C5 G5	A5 F5	C5 G5

Verse 1

|A5   F5 |C5   G5 |
I wrote her off for the tenth time today
|A5   F5 |C5   G5 |
And practiced all the things I would say.
|A5   F5 |C5   G5 |
But she came over, I lost my nerve,
|A5   F5 |C5   G5 |
I took her back and made her dessert.

Verse 2

Now I know I'm being used,
That's okay man 'cause I like the abuse.
Well, I know she's playing with me,
That's okay 'cause I've got no self esteem.

Chorus 1

     A5   F5 |C5   G5 |A5
Oh, way-o,___ yeah,___ yeah,___
     F5 |C5   G5 |
Oh___ yeah, yeah.___   *(Play x2)*

Verse 3

We make plans to go out at night,
I wait till two then I turn out the light.
This rejection's got me so low,
If she keeps it up I just might tell her so.

Chorus 2

As Chorus 1

Bridge 1

|D5   Bb5 |F5   C5 |D5
When she's saying, all that she wants only me,
       Bb5 |F5   C5 |
Then I wonder why she sleeps with my friends.
|D5   Bb5 |F5   C5 |D5
When she saying, all men are like a dis - ease,
       Bb5 |F5   C5 |
Then I wonder how much more I can spend.
|D5   Bb5 |F5   C5 |D5
Well, I guess I should stick up for my - self,
       Bb5 |F5   C5 |
But I really think it's better this way.
|D5   Bb5 |
The more you suffer,
C5   G5 |F5 |F5 C5/G |
The more it shows you really care, right? Yeah.

© COPYRIGHT 1994 GAMETE MUSIC IN
KOBALT MUSIC PUBLISHING LIMITE
ALL RIGHTS RESERVED. INTERNATIONAL COPYRIGHT SECURE

Link		A5 F5		C5 G5		A5 F5		C5 G5	

Verse 4

Now I'll relate, this little bit
That happens more than I'd like to admit.
Late at night, she knocks on my door,
She's drunk again and looking to score.

Verse 5

Now I know, I should say no, but
That's kind of hard when she's ready to go
I may be dumb, but I'm not a dweeb,
I'm just a sucker with no self esteem.

Chorus 3   As Chorus 1

Bridge 2   As Bridge 1

 Introduction

This is The Offspring's punk-rock hit from 1993, and it's a great song for putting your power chords into action.

Which Root?

Although the chord sequence—A, F, C and G—is used most of the way through the song with only minor variations, it's interesting how much bigger the chorus sounds than the verse.

Some of this is down to the F being played in a higher position than it is in the verse. Try it out for yourself, and make sure you can hear when the high voicing (fifth string root) is being played and when the lower voicing (sixth string root) is. It's an important skill to be able to recognise different chord voicings—your cover versions will sound so much more like the original recordings if you put the power chords in the right place.

C/G

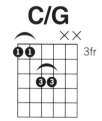

35

 Rhythm

The other really big component to this song is the rhythm. The verses are in a very tight and rhythmic style, so make sure you have your outer palm (strumming hand) resting on the strings near the bridge to create a cool palm mute and make sure that you are still covering every string during the rests, as any uncovered notes will create feedback if you're using a lot of distortion.

For the chorus, take off the palm mute and go for it—play it strongly but don't bash the strings or you won't get a thick sound—the strings will rattle on the fret and your tone will suffer!

Verse + Chorus Sequences

Of course there are some variations on the rhythm patterns below, but the patterns shown below are fairly consistent, so start with them and listen to the track and see if you can pick up some of the variations.

Verse

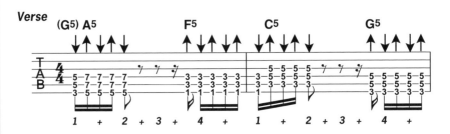

Chorus

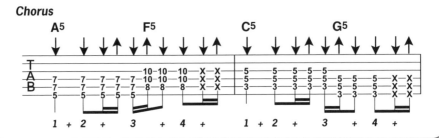

Sunshine Of Your Love

Words & Music by Jack Bruce, Pete Brown & Eric Clapton

 ## Introduction

This is an all-time classic rock blues track, covered by many garage bands since it was written in 1967 by Cream—Eric Clapton's superstar trio with Ginger Baker and Jack Bruce.

 ## Riff 1

There are a few ways of playing the main riff. I started out (as many do) playing a simpler version that I worked out by ear, basically following the bassline:

Clapton uses a variation which is a little harder and involves mixing up two-note chords and single notes with some trills too—it will take a little more practice but it's a lot of fun.

Sunshine Of Your Love

Words & Music by Jack Bruce, Pete Brown & Eric Clapton

riff 1 ⌐————————————————————————¬

Intro   ‖: D C D   A   G♯ │ G   D   F   D :‖ *Play x4*

Verse 1

riff 1 (Play x4)
It's getting near dawn,
When lights close their tired eyes,
I'll soon be with you, my love,
To give you my dawn surprise.

riff 2 ⌐————————————————————————¬

│ G5 F5 G5 D C♯ │ C   G   A♯   G │
I'll be with you darlin' soon,
riff 2   **riff 1 (Play x2)**
I'll be with you when the stars start falling.

Chorus 1

A5   │C5   G5   │
  I've been waiting so long,
A5   │C5   G5   │
   To be where I'm going,
A5   │C5   G5   │A   A
   In the sunshine of your love.____

Link 1   **riff 1 (Play x1)**

Verse 2

I'm with you my love,
The light's shining through on you.
Yes, I'm with you my love,
It's the morning and just we two.
I'll stay with you darling now,
I'll stay with you till my seeds are dried up.

Chorus 2   As Chorus 1

Guitar solo   As Verse 1
As Chorus 1

Link 2   **riff 1 (Play x2)**

Verse 3   As Verse 2

Chorus 3

I've been waiting so long,
I've been waiting so long,
I've been waiting so long,
To be where I'm going,
In the sunshine of your love.

© COPYRIGHT 1967 & 1996 WARNER/CHAPPELL MUSIC LIMITED/ERIC CLAPTON
ALL RIGHTS RESERVED. INTERNATIONAL COPYRIGHT SECURED

Outro
(Double time)

𝄆: A5 | A5 :𝄇 *Play x4 to fade*

Beginner

Intermediate

Intermediate +

TAB

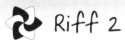

Riff 2

The pattern of this second riff is exactly the same as the pattern of Riff 1 (the main riff). The only difference it that we have now moved down a string, and are now using power chords on the first four notes. Riff 2 is played twice before returning to Riff 1, which then leads into the chorus.

G5   F5 G5

Chorus

The chorus is played with barre chords but it's totally fine to play with open chords, especially if you are doing the simplified riff. Below is the rhythm for these chords. The chords in bar 2 (below) are played on beats 1 and 3, and you should mute the strings with your outer palm on beats 2 and 4. Put in a bit of energy when you mute the chords—you will probably get a little 'hit' noise from the mute, but that's absolutely fine!

A5

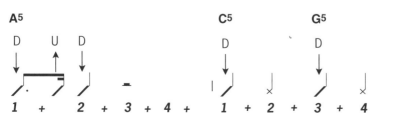

Should I Stay Or Should I Go

Words & Music by Mick Jones & Joe Strummer

Beginner

Intermediate

Intermediate +

TAB

Intro

riff
‖: D   G | D   N.C. :‖ *Play x4*

Verse 1

D N.C. | D   G | D
Darling you got to let me know:
N.C. | D   G | D
Should I stay or should I go?
N.C. | G   F | G
If you say that you are mine
N.C. | D   G | D
I'll be here 'til the end of time.
N.C. | A   A7
So you got to let me know:
N.C. | D   G | D
Should I stay or should I go?

Verse 2

It's always tease, tease, tease;
You're happy when I'm on my knees.
One day is fine, the next is black,
So if you want me off your back,
Well, come on and let me know:
Should I stay or should I go?

Chorus 1

N.C. | D   G | D
Should I stay or should I go now?
                       | D   G | D
Should I stay or should I go now?
                 | G   F | G
If I go there will be trouble,
                 | D   G | D
And if I stay it will be double.
              A | A   D   G | D
So come on and let me know.

Verse 3

This indecision's bugging me   *(esta undecision me molesta)*;
If you don't want me, set me free *(si no me quieres, librame)*.
Exactly who am I'm supposed to be? *(Digame que tengo ser)*.
Don't you know which clothes even fit me?
(¿Saves que robas me queurda?)
Come on and let me know *(me tienes que desir)*
Should I cool it or should I blow? *(¿Me debo ir o quedarme?)*

Instrumental As Verse 1

Chorus 2

Should I stay or should I go now? *(¿Yo me frio o lo sophlo?)*
Should I stay or should I go now? *(¿Yo me frio o lo sophlo?)*
If I go there will be trouble *(si me voy va ver peligro)*,
And if I stay it will be double *(si me quedo es doble)*.
So you gotta let me know *(me tienes que decir)*:
Should I cool it or should I blow? *(¿Yo me frio o lo sophlo?)*

© COPYRIGHT 1982 NINEDEN LIMITED. UNIVERSAL MUSIC PUBILSHING LIMITED.
ALL RIGHTS RESERVED. INTERNATIONAL COPYRIGHT SECURED.

Chorus 3
Should I stay or should I go now? *(¿Yo me frio o lo sophlo?)*
If I go there will be trouble *(si me voy va ver peligro)*,
And if I stay it will be double *(si me quedo es doble)*.
So you gotta let me know *(me tienes que decir)*:
Should I stay or should I go?

Introduction

This is The Clash's iconic single—if any of you young whippersnappers
haven't yet heard The Clash, go and buy yourself a copy of *London Calling* or
Combat Rock (which this song is taken from) right away!

Verse

There are simple open chords used in this song, played using a clean
sound, but with the amplifier tuned up loud enough so it starts getting
crunchy (or add a little overdrive if you don't want to upset your
neighbours!). Start with an up-strum on the 'and' after 1, and make
sure you mute all the strings (with the outside palm of your strumming
hand) after the first beat of the second bar.

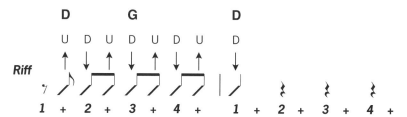

Chorus

In the chorus things get a little more energetic, and the rhythm goes to
double time—twice as fast. The strumming gets pretty frantic but it's
using a hopefully familiar strumming pattern, D DU UD ('Old Faithful').

Note that the G to F movement in the chorus is usually played with
both chords as barre chords. G is just the same as F but up two frets,
but you could play the G open if you are not comfortable with that yet.

Watch out at the end of the chorus, as the riff starts right after the lyrics
end—so you'll only play the A chord for beat 1, as the very next up-
strum will be the D chord starting the riff

Beginner

Intermediate

Intermediate +

TAB

Beginner

Intermediate

Intermediate

Intermediate +

TAB

Smells Like Teen Spirit

Words & Music by Kurt Cobain, Dave Grohl & Krist Novoselic

```
Chord Sequence Throughout
| F5        B♭5    | A♭5      D♭5     |
```

Intro
Play Sequence x6
Play **riff 1** x2

Verse 1
w/ riff 1
Load up on guns and bring your friends,
It's fun to lose and to pretend.
She's overboard and self-assured, oh no,
I know I know, a dirty word.

Pre-chorus 1
w/ riff 2
Hello, hello, hello, how low.
Hello, hello, hello, how low.
Hello, hello, hello, how low.
Hello, hello, hello,

Chorus 1
With the lights out, it's less dang'rous,
Here we are now, entertain us.
I feel stupid and contagious,
Here we are now, entertain us.
A mullato, an albino,
A mosquito, my libido, Yeah.

Link 1
```
| F5 (E) (F)  G♭5   | F5  (E) (F) B♭5     A♭5  |
| F5 (E) (F)  G♭5   | F5  (E) (F) B♭5 A5  A♭5  |
```

Verse 2
I'm worse at what I do best,
And for this gift I feel blessed.
Our little group has always been,
And always will until the end.

Pre-chorus 2
As Pre-chorus 1

Chorus 2
As Chorus 1

Link 2
As Link 1

Instrumental
Play Sequence x10

Verse 3
And I forget just what it takes,
And yeah, I guess, it makes me smile.
I found it hard, it's hard to find,
Oh well, whatever, never mind.

Pre-chorus 3
As Pre-chorus 1

Chorus 3
As Chorus 1

© COPYRIGHT 1991 MJ TWELVE MUSIC/THE END OF MUSIC/
PRIMARY WAVE TUNES/MURKY SLOUGH MUSIC (BMI).
EMI VIRGIN MUSIC LIMITED/WARNER/CHAPPELL MUSIC NORTH AMERICA LIMITED/
FINTAGE PUBLISHING B.V.
ALL RIGHTS RESERVED. INTERNATIONAL COPYRIGHT SECURED.

Outro   A denial, a denial, a denial, a denial,
A denial, a denial, a denial, a denial, denial.

 # Introduction

This is the song that defined the grunge generation, and took Nirvana on to worldwide domination.

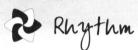 # Rhythm

The main rhythm part uses regular power chords—there's nothing too difficult at all here, but make sure you mute the thickest string with the tip of your 1st finger when playing Root 5 power chords (e.g. on the B♭ and D♭ chords). Also make sure that you are muting all the unplayed strings with the underneath of your first finger or it'll sound awful! The Root 6 power chords often become unintentional sus4 chords—this happens because Kurt Cobain played with lots of energy, pressing a little hard and accidentally pressing down the third string! If you want to be super authentic you might like to try and copy it, but it's better to just give it loads of energy and you'll probably do it by accident too.

The chord sequence in this song is distinctive, but the thing that will really make it sound like the record is the rhythm. I've written out exactly what is played at the start of the song—it doesn't change much throughout the song, but because of Kurt Cobain's quite loose style of guitar playing, there are some bits where the pattern varies a little.

To get the muted hits (X), just release the pressure on your power chord while still letting your fingers touch the strings. You will see that I've notated the open strings (O) which Cobain hit when moving from the B♭ to the A♭, which will make it sound properly authentic and also make the chord change a load easier too! As usual, the strategy is slow and accurate practice, so make sure you're playing the riff correctly at a slow tempo before speeding it up.

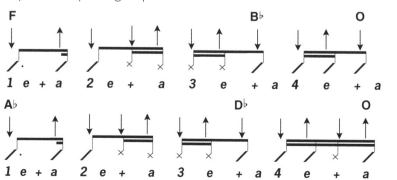

Beginner

Intermediate

Intermediate +

TAB

 Dynamics

One of the key elements to look at here is the change in dynamics, which is a Nirvava trademark: quiet verses and HUGE choruses! You will need some kind of distortion pedal as you will be playing the riff the same way with a clean sound for the intro and then kicking into a big distorted sound for the main strumming riff. It then drops down again to for the verse.

Riff 1

In the verses the bass still drives along but the guitar drops down to play a very simple little two-note figure.

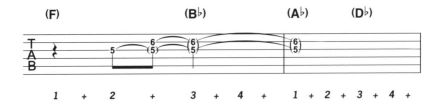

To get the right sound you will need a chorus effects pedal—the one used by Kurt Cobain was the EH Small Clone, a great chorus pedal, but you can get the sound with other pedals: as a starting point, set the rate/speed pretty slow but pulsing, around 11 o'clock and with the depth pretty wide but not wobbly—probably around 1 or 2. Once you have the right sound, the line itself is easy to play.

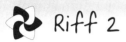 Riff 2

In the pre-chorus, Cobain plays more notes and the distorted electric comes in again too.

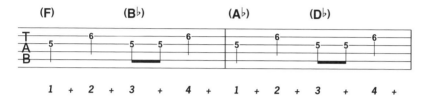

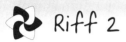 The Link

The other section that needs attention is the Link—as well as the power chords we have a bend on the 3rd fret, which you have to jump to. This can be tricky if you're leaping about the stage like Nirvana! You'll probably want to play the bend with your 2nd finger, although it's tricky with any finger! The bass plays some notes other than the root note too, so don't let that put you off if you are jamming along with the recording.

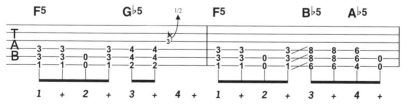

The solo is a very easy one to work out, so please have a go at working it out on your own. You want a hint? It's mostly on String 3 and uses some open strings...now go for it!

Song 2

Music by Damon Albarn, Graham Coxon, Alex James & David Rowntree

Beginner

Intermediate

Intermediate +

TAB

Intro

riff

‖: F5   E♭5 | A♭5   B♭5 C5 :‖

riff (x2)

Whoo hoo, Whoo hoo.
Whoo hoo, Whoo hoo.

Verse 1

riff (x4)

I got my head checked
By a jumbo jet.
It wasn't easy
But nothing is, no.

Chorus 1

riff (x3)

Whoo hoo, when I feel heavy metal,
Whoo hoo, and I'm pins and I'm needles,
Whoo hoo, well, I lie and I'm easy

F5   A♭5   D♭5
All of the time but I am never sure why I need you,

D♭5
  Pleased to meet you.

Link 1

riff (x2)

Verse 2

I got my head done
When I was young,
It's not my problem,
It's not my problem.

Chorus 2

As Chorus 1

Outro

riff (x4)   (Vocals ad lib.)

|F5 |

© COPYRIGHT 1997 EMI MUSIC PUBLISHING LIMITED.
ALL RIGHTS IN THE U.S. AND CANADA CONTROLLED AND ADMINISTERED BY EMI BLACKWOOD MUSIC INC.
ALL RIGHTS RESERVED. INTERNATIONAL COPYRIGHT SECURED.

Beginner

Intermediate

Intermediate +

TAB

 ## Introduction

Blur's simplest and most successful song is a perfect tune for beginners—just a few simple power chords and away you go!

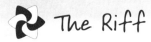 ## The Riff

The most important thing here (other than knowing your power chords) is to get the rhythm right. Below is the TAB of the riff with the rhythm count underneath. I would suggest playing it very slowly and counting along to make sure you have the rhythm correct. Only once you're confident with it should you play along with the record. I find it a lot easier to play these power chords with fingers 1 and 4 (rather than thc usual 1 and 3) but see what feels good for you.

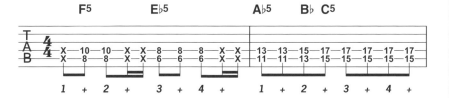

Many software programs (like *Transcribe!* or *Audacity*) are able to slow down recordings so you don't have to play along at full speed right away— this is ideal if you can't quite make the chord changes quickly enough. Slow the track down to 60% or whatever it takes for you to be able to play along, and gradually speed the track up until you are going at full speed.

 ## Tone

The guitar sound changes with the sections in this song—for the verses it's a clean sound, while distortion is added for the chorus. You can hear the huge jump in tone in the intro too—it's a wonderfully chaotic fuzzy mess of brilliance! To get that kind of distortion you'll need distortion built into your amplifier or an effects pedal (stomp box) or both. Because different guitars and amps sound so different I can't suggest exact settings but for the dirty sound, the distortion/gain/overdrive/fuzz should be up pretty high.

Teenage Kicks

Words & Music by John O'Neill

Intro

‖: D5 | D5   C#5 | B5 | B5   C#5 :‖

Verse 1

D5 | D5   C#5 |
A teenage dream's so hard to beat
B5 | B5   C#5 |
Every time she walks down the street.
D5 | D5   C#5 |
Another girl in the neighbourhood,
B5 | B5   A5 |
Wish she was mine, she looks so good.

Chorus 1

G5 | G5
I wanna hold her, wanna hold her tight,
G#5 | A5   A5
Get teenage kicks right through the night.

Verse 2

I wanna call her on the telephone,
Have her over 'cause I'm all alone.
I need excitement, oh, I need it bad,
And it's the best I've ever had.

Chorus 2   As Chorus 1

Link 1   ‖: D5 | D5   C#5 | B5 | B5   C#5 :‖

Verse 3   As Verse 1

Chorus 3   As Chorus 1

Verse 4   As Verse 2

Guitar Solo

| D5 | D5   C#5 | B5 | B5   C#5 |
| D5 | D5   C#5 | B5 | B5   A5 |

Chorus 4

I wanna hold you, wanna hold you tight,
Get teenage kicks right through the night, alright!

Outro

| D5 | G5 | A5   D5 | *(Let final chord ring)*

© COPYRIGHT 1978 WEST BANK SONGS LTD.
UNIVERSAL/MCA MUSIC LIMITED.
ALL RIGHTS RESERVED. INTERNATIONAL COPYRIGHT SECURED.

Introduction

Released in 1978 by the Undertones, this song became a true icon of the Punk movement.

Chord Choices

There are two raucous guitars in this tune: one playing power chords and the other playing a mix of power chords and regular barre chords. I would recommend playing just power chords, which will sound better if you're performing solo.

If you choose to play full barre chords, the B5 will become Bm and the others will be major chords, except the C#5 which needs to stay as a C#5 chord (both major and minor will sound weird!)

There is also a little Dsus4 riff that appears in a couple of breaks—for this, just add your little finger on the 8th fret of string 2. You'll have to listen out for how and when to use it, but it shouldn't be too tricky to figure out how to play it now you know what it is!

When there are two chords in a bar, the second chord is just played on beat 4, usually just the once as a transition chord. Listen to the original recording and you'll hear it clearly.

Rhythm

After doing a little video research, it would seem that one guitarist is playing all down-strums and the other is mixing up down- and up-strums! It's quite uncommon but I suspect that is contributing to the raw, awesome energy of the track. The song uses a two bar pattern and although it's written below as a combination of down- and up-strums, try playing with all downs too as it will have more energy! Of course, when you are playing the verses with the 'step-down' chords you should just play down-strums on beats 3 and 4.

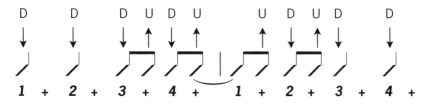

Beginner

Intermediate

Intermediate +

TAB

49

The Ballad Of Jayne

Words & Music by Kelly Nickels, Tracii Guns, Mick Cripps,
Steve Riley & Philip Lewis

Beginner

Intermediate

Intermediate

Intermediate +

TAB

Intro

| Dsus4 C5 | Dsus4 C5 | Dsus4 C5 |

| G | C | G | Dsus4 C5 |

Verse 1

      G   C   G | Dsus4 C5 |
Well, she was always something special,

      G   C   G | Dsus4 C5 |
A diamond shining bright in the rain.

      G   C   G | Dsus4 C5 |
And every - body dreams of angels.

Pre-chorus 1

    D   D
  No   one would ever know

Em   C
   How much I love you so.

Chorus 1

       G   C(add9)
Now it all seems funny, kinda like a dream,

G   C(add9)
Things ain't always what they seem.

      G   C(add9)   G   C(add9)
What a shame,   what happened to Jayne.

Link 1

| D Dsus4 D | D Dsus4 D | D |

| Dsus4 C5 | Dsus4 C5 | Dsus4 C5 |

Verse 2

You were always on my mind, shine like summer days in the sun.
Slowly wishes turn to sadness, time don't heal a broken gun.

Pre-chorus 2

    D   D
  I wish   I never let you go,

| Em7   D | C(add9)
Even now I just want you to know.

Chorus 2

That it all seems funny, kinda like a dream,
Things ain't always what they seem.
What a shame, what happened to Jayne.

Link 2

| D Dsus4 D | D Dsus4 D | D Dsus4 D | D |

| Dsus4 C5 | Dsus4 C5 | Dsus4 C5 |

Guitar solo

| G | C | G | Dsus4 C5 |

| G | C | G | Dsus4 C5 |

| Am   G/B | C | G | G |

| Am   G/B | C | D | D |

| Dsus4 C5 | Dsus4 C5 | Dsus4 C5 |

© COPYRIGHT 1990 AL SNUG MUSIC.
UNIVERSAL MUSIC PUBLISHING LIMITED.
ALL RIGHTS RESERVED. INTERNATIONAL COPYRIGHT SECURED.

Beginner
Intermediate
Intermediate +
TAB

Verse 3
Now she's breaking hearts in heaven,
Shining bright in the sky.
I still hear her voice in the wind,
I still think of you in the night.

Pre-chorus 3
chords as pre-chorus 2
Well I guess you'll never know
How much I need her so.

Chorus 3
But it all seems funny, kinda like a dream,
Things ain't always what they seem.
      G   C(add9)
What a shame,
    | D Dsus4 D | D Dsus4 D | Em D | C(add9)
What happened to Jayne.
Now it all seems funny, kinda like a dream,
Things ain't always what they seem.
                                                  G
What a shame, what happened to Jayne, what happened to Jayne.

Introduction

LA Guns are an essential part of rock music history, as they were founding members of the LA glam-rock scene which bought us Guns N' Roses, Poison, Skid Row and many more. The history of the period makes for very entertaining reading too! Note that if you are playing along with the original recording, you'll need to tune your guitar down a semitone (use your tuner: Eb, Ab, Db, Gb, Bb, Eb).

Chords

The chords are all pretty familiar, but there is an interesting little riff based on a C chord shape that slides up two frets, and which first appears in the intro.

Intro

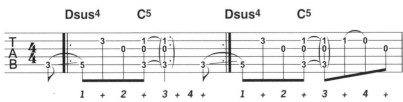

51

Beginner

Intermediate

Intermediate +

TAB

♻ Picked Strumming

The verse uses a kind of picked strumming, where some notes are picked out amongst the strums—it'll be easiest to figure out a summarised version and then work out the variations.

As well as the main acoustic part there is more strumming, played most of the way through using a simple pattern, which compliments the picked one shown above.

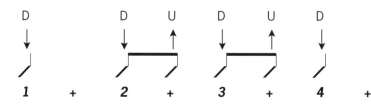

♻ Chorus

In the chorus there is a strummed guitar playing the pattern but the other acoustic guitar part changes to another nice strummed and 'picked out' pattern shown below (it's also doubled by an electric guitar).

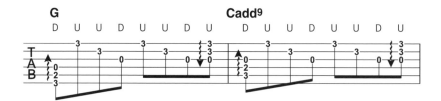

You'll also hear some power chords and single note runs in there too—now you know the chords and the structure you shouldn't find it too tricky to work out by ear! I still remember working the solo out as a teenager and feeling very proud of myself!

I Remember You

Words & Music by Rachel Bolan & Dave Sabo

 ## Introduction

This song was a huge hit for Skid Row in 1989 and has all the trademarks of the hair metal genre: an acoustic ballad with big power chords, lots of squealing guitars and a really powerful vocal!

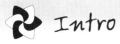 ### Intro

The intro of this song uses a couple of trademark phases which sound cool and are not too difficult to play. As usual the trick is to practise slowly and pay real attention to the timing. Playing along with the slowed-down original recording (using software) is a great way to get the timing and feel right. Looking at the TAB, it seems very complicated, but note that this is an accurate transcription of the first time it's heard on the recording, and it's a little different each time. Most of the individual notes are just what happened to be strummed and it won't sound wrong if you hit some other strings at the same time, or even different notes—the thing to remember is to keep your strumming hand moving consistently and to make it flow.

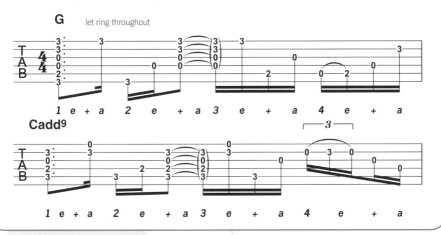

Acoustic Vs. Electric

One of the key elements of this genre is the mixture of acoustic and electric guitar parts. The acoustic guitar strums happily away on the open chords, while the electric guitar gets busy playing power chords, with the occasional single-note line, alongside lead licks and pick scratches into the chords. Both work really well, so I'd recommend checking out both.

53

I Remember You

Words & Music by Rachel Bolan & Dave Sabo

Beginner

Intermediate

Intermediate

Intermediate +

TAB

Intro
| G | C(add9) | G | C(add9) |

Verse 1

G   C(add9)
Woke up to the sound of pouring rain,
G   C(add9)
The wind would whisper and I'd think of you
G   C(add9)
And all the tears you cried that called my name.
D   C(add9)
And when you needed me I came through.

Verse 2

I paint a picture of the days gone by,
When love went blind and you would make me see.
I'd stare a lifetime into your eyes
So that I knew that you were there for me,
D   C(add9)
Time after time you were there for me.

Chorus 1

G   D
Remember yesterday,   walking hand in hand,
Em   C(add9)
Love letters in the sand, I remember you.
G   D
Through the sleepless nights,   through every endless day,
Em   C(add9)   (G)
I'd wanna hear you say, I remember___ you.

Link
| (G) | C(add9) | G | C(add9) |

Verse 3

We spent the summer with the top rolled down,
Wished ever-after would be like this.
You said 'I love you babe', without a sound,
I said I'd give my life for just one kiss,
I'd live for your smile and die for your kiss.

Chorus 2

As Chorus 1

Bridge

(G)   G   Am
              We've had our share of hard times,
Em
But that's the price we paid.
Am   D
And through it all, we kept the promise that we made,
D
I swear you'll never be lonely.

Guitar solo

|: G | C(add9) :| *(Play x3)*

|: D | C(add9) :||: G | C(add9) :|

© COPYRIGHT 1990 NEW JERSEY UNDERGROUND MUSIC, INC./BMG GOLD SONGS.
BMG RIGHTS MANAGEMENT (US) LLC.
ALL RIGHTS RESERVED. INTERNATIONAL COPYRIGHT SECURED.

Verse 4 Woke up to the sound of pouring rain,
Washed away a dream of you.
But nothing else could ever take you away,
'Cause you'll always be my dream come true,
Oh my darling, I love you.

Chorus 3 As Chorus 1

Chorus 4 As Chorus 1

C(add9)   C(add9) | C(add9) G | D   Em
I remember you._____
C(add9)   G   D Em C(add9)
Oh____ yeah.

Outro | G | C(add9) | G | C(add9) | G |

❧ Electric Rhythm

In the pre-chorus and chorus, the electric guitar is picking up on
various rhythmic pushes and accents, which are much easier learned
by listening to the song than by reading them from notation. There are
a few electric guitar parts playing at the same time—all doing little fills
here and there—so you can pick up as much or as little as you like.
I've written out one of the electric parts to get you started, but go and
explore it on your own too!

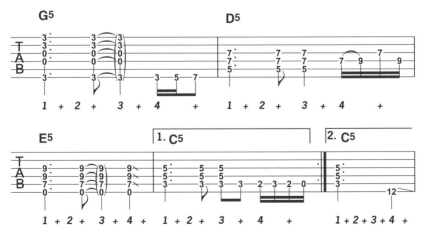

The lead solo is beyond the scope of this book but it's a classic from the
period and well worth looking up if you are getting into this genre!

INTERMEDIATE STAGE

 ## Introduction

Now that you're not a beginner any more (congratulations, by the way!) we're going to learn some more advanced songs and skills. Above all, these Intermediate songs will help you develop your ability to play barre chords. I spent many years avoiding barre chords, and worrying that I wasn't ready, but my advice to you is to get stuck into them as soon as you are confident with all your beginner techniques.

At this stage, a big part of your studies will be learning to recognise which chords to play as barre chords, and which to play 'open'. The matter is made more interesting by the fact that many chords can be played both as open chords and as barre chords. You must decide which voicings to use in each situation. There is often no right or wrong, although there may be creative or practical reasons that lead you to choose one voicing over another.

Over the page, you will find a guide on playing the eight main barre chord shapes. When you start learning how to play barre chords, it is likely that you will find the E-shape chords (with the root on the 6th string) easiest to play, and will prefer to play them, rather than the A-shape chords. This is absolutely fine. As you get used to the A-shape barre chords, your options will increase and you will choose your voicings accordingly.

You may find that a song sounds better if all the chords are played as barre chords. At other times you will play most of the chords open, and only barre when you have to. Do what you feel most comfortable with to start with, and as your playing develops, choose the voicing that sounds best!

Also in this section I will be introducing some sixteenth-note strumming patterns. Remember that the trick to playing them is to practise them slowly and carefully and repeat them many times. 'Practice makes permanent' (not 'perfect' as is so often quoted!), and you should be aiming to practise a pattern until it feels completely natural and instinctive. A good test is to keep playing a pattern while having a conversation with someone. If you can do that then you'll have the pattern well and truly 'in the bag'.

Intermediate Stage:
Your Notes

BARRE CHORDS

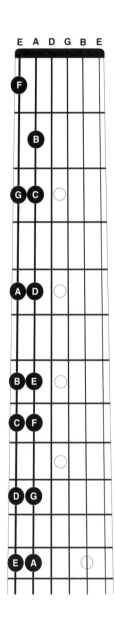

Getting Started

On the facing page are the eight essential barre chord grips. You must memorise these grips, along with the corresponding bass notes on the thickest two strings.

To find a chord, first locate the root note. If the root note is a sharp or a flat (e.g. F♯ or B♭), then move up or down one fret accordingly (sharp—move towards the bridge, flat—move towards the nut). Then use the appropriate chord shape (major, minor, 7th or minor 7th), using E-shape grips when the root note is on the 6th string, and A-shape grips when the root is on the 5th string.

If you have any problems playing any of these chords, please check out the relevant lessons in the Intermediate Method section of the web site (starting with IM-111 and IM-131).

E-Shape Barre Chords

Major **Minor** **7** **Minor 7**

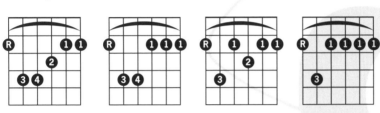

A-Shape Barre Chords

Major **Minor** **7** **Minor 7**

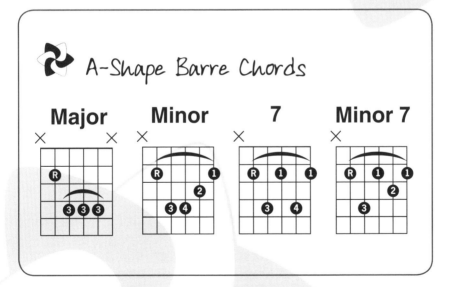

(R = Root note)

Alison

Words & Music by Elvis Costello

Beginner

Intermediate

Intermediate +

TAB

Intro

| E/B   B | G♯m A C♯m B | F♯m G♯m | G♯m B |

Verse 1

       A   **E**
Oh it's so funny to be seeing you after so long girl,

               A
And with the way you look I understand

  | **G♯m**   **C♯m   B** |
That you were not im - pressed,

A | **G♯m**   **C♯m** |
    But I heard you let that little friend of mine

D | **Bsus⁴ B** |
    Take off your party dress.

A | **G♯m**   **C♯m**
    I'm not going to get too senti - mental

B |**A** | **G♯m   C♯m   B** |
Like those other sticky valentines.

A | **G♯m**   **C♯m**
    'Cause I don't if you are loving some - body

|**D** | **Bsus⁴ B**
I only know, it isn't mine.

Chorus 1

A |**E**   **A** |**A**   **B**   **G♯m** |**G♯ C♯m**
Ali - son, I know this world is kil - ling you,

B |**A**   **E** |**A**   **B** |**E**
Oh Ali - son,   my aim is true.

Verse 2

Well I see you've got a husband now,
Did he leave your pretty fingers
Lying in the wedding cake?
You used to hold him right in your hand.
I'll bet he took all he could take.
Sometimes I wish that I could stop you from talking
When I hear the silly things that you say.
I think somebody better put out the big light,
'Cause I can't stand to see you this way.

Chorus 2

A |**E**   **A** |**A**   **B**   **G♯m** |**G♯ C♯m**
Ali - son, I know this world is kil - ling you,

B |**A**   **E** |**A**   **B** |**E**   **A** |
Oh Ali - son,   my aim is true.

Outro

‖: **D**   **B** |**E** **A** :‖ *Repeat to fade*
    My aim is true.

© COPYRIGHT 1977 SIDEWAYS SONGS
PUBLISHED BY UNIVERSAL MUSIC PUBLISHING MGB LTD
ALL RIGHTS RESERVED. INTERNATIONAL COPYRIGHT SECURED.

Introduction

Elvis Costello's influences are a mixture of rock 'n' roll, punk and country, all of which combine in this classic hit from 1977.

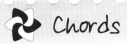

Chords

The guitar part on the recording mainly plays lead lines with some occasional chords, but this song is a great vehicle for learning your barre chords. The lead lines in this song are really satisfying to play and well worth working out if you are going to perform the song with a band, though they're beyond the scope of this book.

I've written out the intro for those who fancy a challenge, although it's fine to leave this section out. The chord part should be played fingerstyle, with your thumb playing the bass, and fingers playing the chords.

Intro Chords

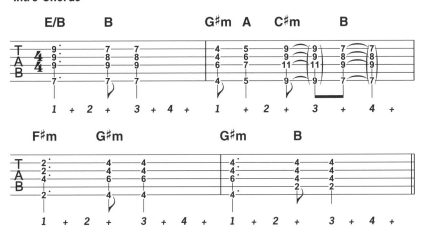

Intro Lead Guitar

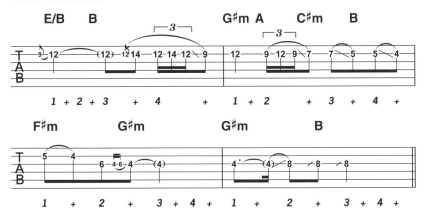

61

Beginner

Intermediate

Intermediate +

TAB

Chorus Rhythm

Assuming that you will be playing barre chords throughout, this song poses some interesting questions as to which chord voicings you should use. For example, after the first B chord there is an A chord, and your natural tendency may lead you to play the A as an open chord, but then you have a tricky jump to the G#m. Perhaps the A is better played as a barre chord at the 5th fret? So which do you use? I can't tell you! You have to try them and see what feels and sounds best to you. There is no right or wrong because we're playing an arrangement of the keyboard part. I've added in a couple of extra strums in bars 1 and 2—they don't feature in the studio recording, but will help you keep time if you're playing solo.

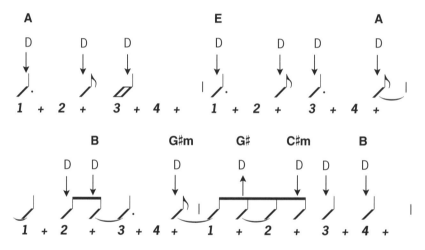

Strumming

The rhythm pattern here works great on its own. The guitar on the recording only plays lead lines, so this pattern gives you the groove with just the guitar. Use all down-strums, and on beats 2 and 4 you can do a muted hit to bring out a percussive backbeat

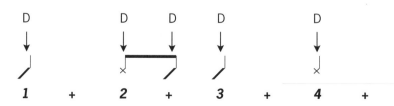

Creep

Words & Music by Albert Hammond, Mike Hazlewood, Thom Yorke, Jonny Greenwood, Colin Greenwood, Ed O'Brien & Phil Selway

Introduction

Radiohead's debut single from 1992 uses the quiet verse / massive chorus arrangement that works so well in many rock hits!

The Intro

The intro guitar part is distinctive and really effective, using regular E-shape barre chords and the occasional sus4, which you get by simply moving your little finger down a string when it's required. It's pretty easy and sounds great. To capture the exact sound on the recording, you might like to add a light tremolo effect.

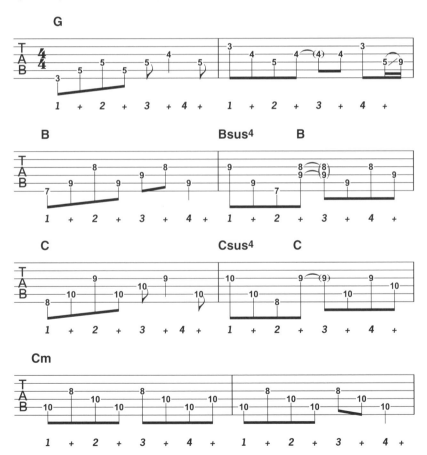

The verses are very similar to the intro, but use different picking and omit some of the sus chords—you might like to work out these variations out, or just make up your own ones as you see fit.

Creep

Words & Music by Albert Hammond, Mike Hazlewood, Thom Yorke, Jonny Greenwood,
Colin Greenwood, Ed O'Brien & Phil Selway

Beginner

Intermediate

Intermediate +

TAB

Intro

| G | G | B | Bsus4 B |

| C | Csus4 C | Cm | Cm |

Verse 1

                 G   G   B
When you were here be - fore,   couldn't look you in the eye,

B   C   C   Cm   Cm
   You're just like an angel,   your skin makes me cry.

                 G   G   B   B
You float like a feather,   In a beautiful world.

              C   Cm   Cm
I wish I was special, you're so very special

Chorus 1

          G   G   B   B
But I'm a creep,   I'm a weirdo.

                    C   C
What the hell am I doing here?

          Cm   Cm
I don't be - long here.

Verse 2

I don't care if it hurts, I wanna have control,
I wanna perfect body, I wanna perfect soul.
I want you to notice when I'm not around,
You're so very special, I wish I was special...

Chorus 2

But I'm a creep, I'm a weirdo.
What the hell am I doing here?

          Cm   Cm
I don't be - long here. Oh, oh.

Bridge

G   G   B   B
She's running out a - gain,

C   C
She's running out

      Cm   Cm
She's run, run, run,

G   G B   B   C   C   Cm   Cm
Run.   Run...

Verse 3

Whatever makes you happy, whatever you want,
You're so very special, I wish I was special...

Chorus 3

But I'm a creep, I'm a weirdo,
what the hell am I doing here?

          Cm   Cm   G
I don't be - long here,   I don't be - long here.

© COPYRIGHT 1992 WARNER/CHAPPELL MUSIC LIMITED/IMAGEM SONGS LIMITED.
ALL RIGHTS RESERVED. INTERNATIONAL COPYRIGHT SECURED.

Chorus

The chorus breaks into some big gnarly power chords that follow the same chord sequence. Just jump on your distortion pedal and thrash it out.

There are some overdubbed octave guitar parts that sneak in during the chorus but they are very subtle and work best as a second guitar part—on their own they sound a little strange. In the Bridge, this octaves idea is explored more and becomes a kind of solo under the vocal, picking out chord tones—it sounds great. I've written out a compilation of some of the melodic lines that I can hear, just to get you started and to show you the key elements of this part.

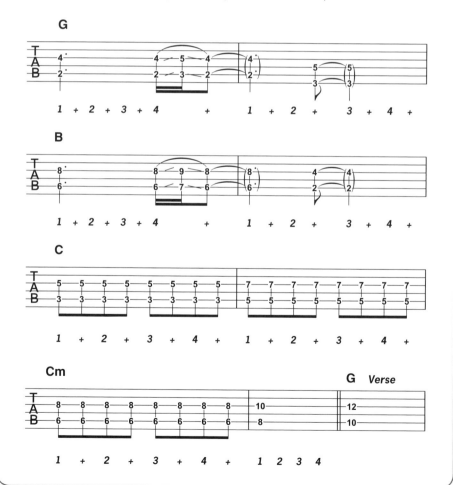

Behind Blue Eyes

Words & Music by Pete Townshend

Beginner

Intermediate

Intermediate +

TAB

Intro

| Esus4 | Esus4 | Esus4 | Esus4 |

Verse 1

```
Em                          G
No one knows what it's like
              D        |Dsus4  D        |Cadd9    Cadd9
To be the bad man,         to be the sad man
         Asus2         Asus2
Behind blue eyes.
```

Verse 2

No one knows what it's like to be hated,
To be fated, to telling only lies.

Chorus 1

```
              C        D        |G     Gsus4  |G
But my dreams  they aren't as empty
              C        D        |E     A/E    |E
As my conscience seems to be.
         Bm    Bm    C    C         D      |Dsus4  D  |
I have hours      only lonely,  my love is vengeance
              Asus2  Asus2  Asus2  Asus2
That's never free.
```

Verse 3

No one knows what it's like to feel these feelings
Like I do, and I blame you!

Verse 4

No one bites back this hard on their anger,
None of my pain and woe can show through.

Chorus 2

As Chorus 1

Link

| E | Bm   A | E | Bm   A |

Bridge

```
E                   |Bm      A              |
  When my fist clenches crack it open
E        |Bm      G      |D       |Bm    A            |D
  Before I use it and lose my cool; when I smile tell me some bad news
         |Bm      A      |E  | Bm   A  |
Before I laugh and act like a fool.
E        |Bm      A      |E        |Bm    G        |D
And if I swallow anything evil, put your finger down my throat;
         |Bm          A          |D
And if I shiver please give me a blanket,
         |Bm          A          |E  |Bm  A |E  |Bm   A  |
Keep me warm, let me wear your coat
```

Link

| B | A   G   D | B | A   G   D |
| B | A   G   D | B | B |

© COPYRIGHT 1971 FABULOUS MUSIC LIMITED
ALL RIGHTS RESERVED. INTERNATIONAL COPYRIGHT SECURED

Outro

No one knows what it's like
To be the bad man, to be the sad man,
Behind blue eyes.

 # Introduction

This classic Who song (later covered by Limp Bizkit) is half-ballad / half-rocker, and features some lovely picked guitar.

 ## Picking Fun

The best known and most recognisable feature of this song is the wonderful acoustic guitar part, written out for you here. It's played with a pick and requires accuracy and good timing to really sound impressive. The chords are not too tricky, so the trick to getting the picking right will be to practise the part slowly and carefully at first (as usual).

Intro

Esus⁴

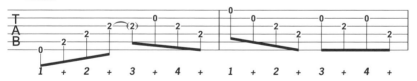

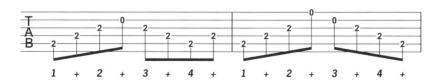

continued...

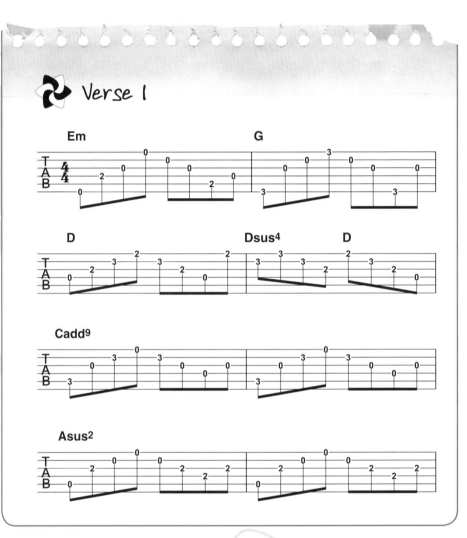

Verse 1

Bridge

Things crank up a notch during the bridge section, with some dirty fuzz electric guitar—note that the acoustic guitar is still strumming away underneath, mostly using the 'Old Faithful' strumming pattern (see the opposite page) but there are some pretty complex changes in rhythm toward the end which you will have to listen to very carefully if you are to pick them up.

Better Man
Words & Music by Eddie Vedder

Introduction

This is Pearl Jam's pop-rock hit, taken from the album *Vitalogy* (1994).

The Riff

One of the coolest things about the main riff is the way it uses one chord shape which simply moves around the neck. It start as a fingerstyle riff but later in the song the same chord grips are strummed.

D/F#

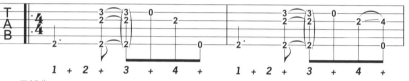

E/G#

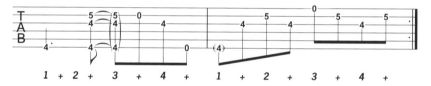

Pre-Chorus

F/A   **G/B**

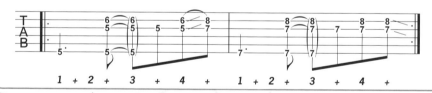

Strumming

The rhythm for most of the strumming sections is 'Old Faithful' yet again. It's amazing how often this strumming pattern turns up, hence its name. Just be careful that when you are strumming the verse chords that the thin E string is muted or it'll sound a bit strange.

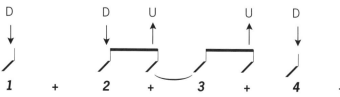

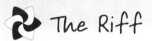

Better Man

Words & Music by Eddie Vedder

Intro

riff

‖: D/F♯ | D/F♯ | E/G♯ | E/G♯ :‖

Verse 1

riff x2

Waitin', watchin' the clock, it's four o'clock, it's got to stop.
Tell him, take no more, she practises her speech.

Pre-Chorus 1

       F/A   G/B
As he opens the door, she rolls over,

       F/A   G/B   G/B
Pre - tends to sleep as he looks her over.

Chorus 1

D |A   G |D
  She lies and says she's in love with him,
           |A   G |
Can't find a better man.

D |A   G |D
  She dreams in colour, she dreams in red,
         |A   Asus⁴ |A
Can't find a better man.___

Asus⁴ |D   Dsus⁴ | D
Can't find a better man.___

Dsus⁴ |A   Asus⁴ | A Asus⁴ |G G
Can't find a better man.___   Oh.

Link 1

Play riff

Verse 2

Talkin' to herself, there's no one else who needs to know,
She tells herself, oh.
Memories back when she was bold and strong
And waiting for the...

Pre-Chorus 2

...world to come along.
Swears she knew it, now she swears he's gone.

Chorus 2

|D   Dsus²|A   G |D
  She lies and   says she's in love with him,
Dsus² |A   G |
Can't find a better man.

|D   Dsus² |A   G |D
  She dreams in   colour, she dreams in red,
Dsus² |A   G |
Can't find a better man.___

© COPYRIGHT 1994 INNOCENT BYSTANDER MUSIC.
SONY/ATV MUSIC PUBLISHING.
ALL RIGHTS RESERVED. INTERNATIONAL COPYRIGHT SECURED.

Chorus 3   She lies and says she still loves him,
Can't find a better man.
She dreams in colour, she dreams in red,

|D Dsus2 |A   Asus4 | A
      Can't   find a better man.___

Asus4 |D   Dsus4| D
Can't find a better man.

Dsus4 |A   Asus4| A Asus4 |
Can't find a better man.___

Link 2 | G | G | G Gsus4 | G |

Chorus 4   She loved him, yeah,
She don't want to leave this way.
She feeds him, yeah,
That's why she'll be back again.

Chorus 5   Can't find a better man.   *(x4)*

Outro   ‖: D | A   G   :‖   *(Play x10)*

| D | A   G | D |

Chorus

The chorus uses more open chords with a lot of sus movements.
There are many variations, but to put you on the right track I have
written out a summarised version of the chorus so you can see how
you might incorporate these sus chords. Hopefully this will help you to
hear these sus chords on the recording and be able to experiment with
them yourself.

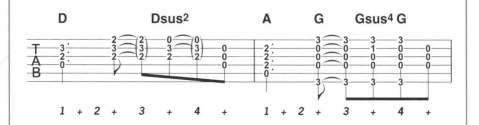

Born To Be Wild

Words & Music by Mars Bonfire

Intro ‖: riff 1 :‖ *(Play x4)*

Verse 1

riff 2 (x4)
Get your motor running,
Head out on the highway,
Looking for adventure
And whatever comes our way.

Pre-chorus 1

|G   A |E5
  Yeah, darling, go and make it happen,
|G   A |E5
  Take the world in a love embrace,
|G   A |E5
  Fire all of your guns at once and
|G   A |E5
  Explode into space.

Verse 2

I like smoke and lightning, heavy metal thunder.
Racing with the wind, and the feeling that I'm under.

Pre-chorus 2 As Pre-chorus 1

Chorus 1

          E
Like a true Nature's child
          G
We were born, born to be wild.
         A
We can climb so high,
G   E5   E5
  I never want to die.
E5   D5   E5   D5
Born to be wild.
E5   D5   E5   D5
Born to be wild.

Organ solo

‖: E | E | E | E   :‖

‖: E7♯9 | E7♯9 | E7♯9 | E7♯9   :‖
                                      Drum fill
| E | E | E | E | E N.C. | N.C. |

Verse 3 As Verse1

Pre-chorus 3 As Pre-chorus 1

Chorus 2 As Chorus 1

© COPYRIGHT 1968 MANITOU MUSIC, USA.
UNIVERSAL/MCA MUSIC LIMITED.
ALL RIGHTS RESERVED. INTERNATIONAL COPYRIGHT SECURED.

Beginner

Intermediate

Intermediate +

TAB

Coda

E5		D5	E5	D5

Born to be wild.

E5		D5	E5	D5

Born to be wild.

‖: E | E | E | E :‖

| E7♯9 | E7♯9 | E7♯9 | E7♯9 | E7♯9 |

Fade out

Introduction

The unofficial biker anthem, Steppenwolf's song was included on the soundtrack to the classic movie *Easy Rider* (1969).

Riff 1

Lets check out Riff 1 first. It's a proper rock riff, based on the blues, and many of you should recognise it as a barre chord version of the 12-Bar Blues Variations lesson in my Beginner's Course! It requires some stretching with the little finger, which will just take a little practice. Don't bother leaving your 3rd finger down as you stretch your pinky up to the 12th fret—it's okay to take it off if that helps you hit the note cleanly!

Riff 2

Once we're into the verses we have some pumping eighth-notes and then the main riff, like this:

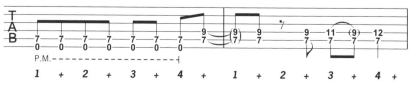

Beginner

Intermediate

Intermediate +

TAB

Pre-Chorus

Things get more interesting when we hit the pre-chorus, though I'll confess that when I played this song as a teenager I left out all the lead lines and just played the chords. I suggest you start the same way, playing the barre chords and ignoring the lead fills at first, only fitting in the lead licks once you can play the chords all the way through.

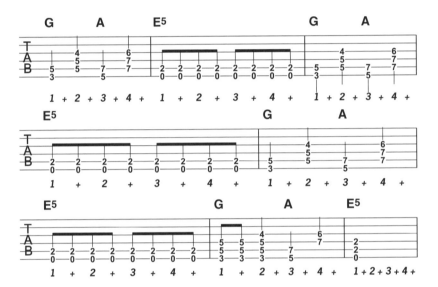

Full version (with licks)

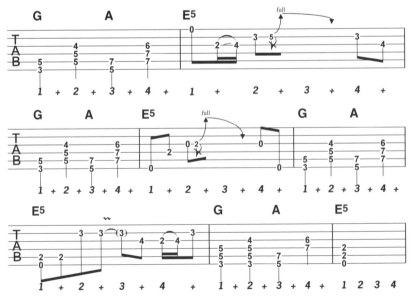

Chorus

When we hit the chorus we have some very specific rhythms at the start, before some big sustained chords. The sustained D5 chord in the chorus is just a standard D, but played without the sixth string.

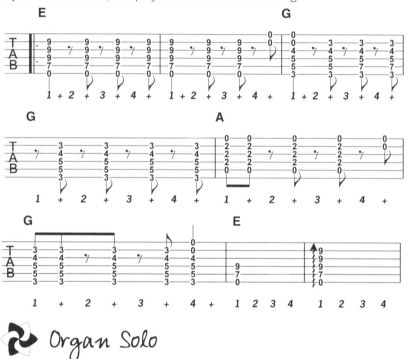

Organ Solo

The rhythm playing behind the organ solo needs to be absolutely watertight and is a great lesson on rhythm playing. You'll need to mute the chord between the up-strums—my advice is to listen to the recording a lot and try to copy what you hear (the way all rock 'n' roll should be learned!). There is also a really funky section using the 'Hendrix' chord, E7♯9.

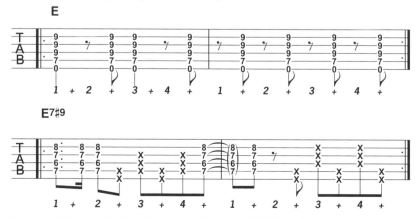

(Don't Fear) The Reaper

Words & Music by Donald Roeser

Intro

riff ——————

‖: A5 G | F6/9 G :‖ *(Play x4)*

Verse 1

riff x4

All our times have come
Here but now they're gone.

Chorus 1

|F   G | Am
Seasons don't fear the reaper,
          |F   E |Am
Nor do the wind, the sun or the rain.
      G |F   G | riff x4
We can be like they are, come on baby.
Don't fear the reaper, baby take my hand.
Don't fear the reaper, we'll be able to fly.
Don't fear the reaper , baby I'm your man.

Link 1

riff x5

La,la la, la, la,
La, la la, la, la. | Am7 | Am7 |
                        (let ring)

Link 2

Play **riff x4**

Verse 2

riff x4

Valentine is done, here but now they're gone.

Chorus 2

|F   G |Am |F   E |Am   G
   Romeo and Juliet are together in eternity. *(Romeo and Juliet)*
|F   G |Am   G
Forty thousand men and women every day, *(Like Romeo and Juliet)*
|F   G |Am   G |F
Forty thousand men and women every day, *(Really find happiness.)*
          G |Am   G |F
Another forty thousand coming every day, *(We can be like they are)*

Chorus 3

G | riff x4
Come on baby
Don't fear the reaper, baby take my hand.
Don't fear the reaper, we'll be able to fly.
Don't fear the reaper, baby I'm your man.

Link 3

As Link 1

Bridge

‖: Fm |Fm | G | G :‖ *(Play x8)*

Link 4

As Link 1

Verse 3

riff x4

Love of two is won, here but now they're gone.

© COPYRIGHT 1978 SONY/ATV TUNES LLC, USA.
SONY/ATV MUSIC PUBLISHING.
ALL RIGHTS RESERVED. INTERNATIONAL COPYRIGHT SECURED.

Chorus 4 Came the last night of sadness,
and it was clear that she couldn't go on.
And the door was open and the wind appeared,
The candles blew and then disappeared,
The curtains flew and then he appeared,

riff cont.

(Saying, "Don't be afraid") Come on baby.
(And she had no fear) and she ran to him,
(Then they started to fly), they looked backward and said goodbye.
(She had become like they are), she had taken his hand,
(She had become like they are), come on, baby,
Don't fear the reaper.

Introduction

One of the all time classic rock songs, this was released in 1976 by Blue
Öyster Cult and immortalised in the hilarious 'More Cowbell!' sketch by Will
Ferrell on *Saturday Night Live*. As brilliant as the whole song is, we're not
going to look in detail at the prog-rock style Bridge section, simply because
it would require a whole heap of TAB and it isn't the most popular part of
the song.

The Riff

The thing everybody wants to learn in this song is the main riff. It's
pretty easy—alongside a few open strings, the only shapes you'll need
are: an A5 chord played with just your 1st finger, followed by an open
G and a two-note F power chord. The hardest part of it is picking the
strings accurately, which will just take practice!

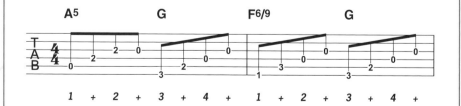

continued...

 Rhythm

As well as the main riff, there are some chord sections too (mainly in the choruses), and these are played as regular power chords, using a pumping eighth-note rhythm with a light palm mute.

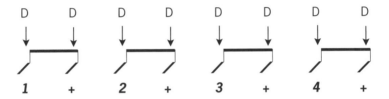

Acoustic Strumming

If you want to strum the song, feel free to experiment with a variety of different strumming patterns. You might like to start off with 'Old Faithful'—this would be my first choice, particularly if I was doing a 'campfire' version of the song on acoustic guitar.

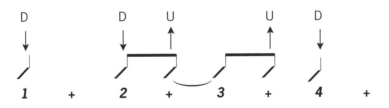

Don't Look Back In Anger
Words & Music by Noel Gallagher

Introduction
One of Oasis' signature songs, this Beatles-influenced track was released at the height of Britpop in 1996.

Barre Chord Grips

This is a great song for learning how to mix your open and barre chords. There are only a few barres—F and Fm—but you'll have to hold them down just long enough for your hand to get a bit achey (if you are new to barre chords).

This song is a great test for your E-shape minor grip, because in the pre-chorus we're playing F and then Fm. If you don't hear the second chord change to the minor, you are probably not holding your barre down hard enough. When the E-shape barre is weak the first note to drop out is the third string—the only note that changes when switching from major to minor.

Bridge Chord

There is one other interesting chord that pops up in the Bridge, which is an E7/G♯. It's not very hard but you may need to practise changing to it from the previous G chord before you get it right. Finger 2 should be lightly touching the fifth string, in order to mute it.

E7/G♯

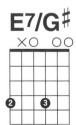

Don't Look Back In Anger

Words & Music by Noel Gallagher

Beginner

Intermediate

Intermediate +

TAB

Intro | C | F | C | F |

Verse 1
```
 C              G          Am
Slip inside the eye of your mind,
            E          F
Don't you know you might find
 G                    |C   Am  G |
   A better place to play.
|C             G          Am
You said that you'd never been,
              E          |F
But all the things that you've seen
 G            |C   Am  G |
Slowly fade away.
```

Bridge 1
```
|F              Fm           |C
So I start a revolution from my bed,
        |F             Fm          |C
'Cause you said the brains I had went to my head.
|F          Fm          |C
Step outside, summertime's in bloom,
 G
Stand up beside the fireplace,
E7/G#
Take that look from off your face,
|Am          G           |F      G   G
You ain't ever gonna burn my heart out.
```

Chorus 1
```
|C  G      |Am     E         |F         G          |C  Am G |
So Sally can wait, she knows it's too late as she's walking on by.
        |C  G    |Am E        |F        G        (C)
Her soul slides away,  but don't look back in anger   I heard you say.
```

Instrumental | C   G | Am   E | F   G | C   Am G |

Verse 2
Take me to the place where you go,
Where nobody knows
If it's night or day.
Please don't put your life in the hands
Of a rock 'n' roll band
Who'll throw it all away.

Bridge 2   As Bridge 1

Chorus 2
So Sally can wait, she knows it's too late
As she's walking on by.
Her soul slides away, but don't look back in anger

© COPYRIGHT 1995 CREATION SONGS LIMITED/OASIS MUSIC (GB).
SONY/ATV MUSIC PUBLISHING.
ALL RIGHTS RESERVED. INTERNATIONAL COPYRIGHT SECURED.

(cont.)

```
        |C   Am  G    |
```
I heard you say.

Guitar solo   Chords as Bridge

Chorus 3   As Chorus 2

Chorus 4   So Sally can wait, she knows it's too late
                    As she's walking on by.
```
        |C   G    |Am                    Fadd9
```
Her soul slides a - way, but don't look back in anger,
```
                          Fm7    Fm7
```
Don't look back in anger
```
        |C   G  | Am   E  | F   Fm |
```
I heard you say.
```
               C
```
At least not to - day.

Finger Lift

At the end of the Bridge Noel Gallagher uses a very cool little trick by lifting the tip of his first finger while playing the F barre chord to reveal the open E (string 6) on the off-beats. It's a good dexterity test as you need to hold the rest of the chord down.

Rhythm

The strumming patterns are very varied in this song and although I've given you a suggested starting point (below) you'll need to explore them yourself. The recorded guitar parts combine rhythms with short lead fills and chord variations, many of which use different strumming patterns. Be aware too that even though it's a sixteenth-note strumming pattern it has a very relaxed feel and shouldn't be rushed.

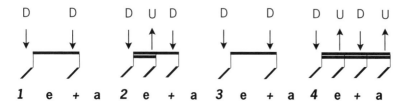

D	D	D	U	D	D	D	D	U	D	U
1	e	+	a	2	e	+	a	3	e	+	a	4	e	+	a

Handbags And Gladrags

Words & Music by Michael D'Abo

Capo Fret

1

Beginner

Intermediate

Intermediate +

TAB

Intro ‖: A   A/G | D/F♯   E7 :‖   *Play x3*

Verse 1
| A   A/G |D/F♯
Ever seen a blind man cross the road
E7sus4 | A A/G | D/F♯   E7sus4 |
Trying to make the other side?
| A   A/G |D/F♯
Ever seen a young girl growin' old
E7sus4 | A A/G | D/F♯   E7sus4 |
Trying to make herself a bride?

Chorus 1
F♯m   E
So what becomes of you   my love,
A   B
When they've finally stripped you of
    D
The handbags and the gladrags
              D/E |A   A/G |
That your poor old Grandad had to sweat to buy you.
|D/F♯ E7 |A A/G | D/F♯   E7 |
Yeah,   yeah.

Verse 2
Once I was a young man
And all I thought I had to do was smile.
Well you are still a young girl
And you've bought everything in style.

Chorus 2
So once you think you're in, you're out,
'Cause you don't mean a single thing without
The handbags and the gladrags
That your poor old Grandad had to sweat to buy you.

Link
| A   A/G | D/F♯   E7 |
| A   A/G | D/F♯   D/E |A   D/E |

Verse 3
Sing a song of six-pence for your sake, and drink a bottle full of rye.
Four and twenty blackbirds in a cake, and bake them all in a pie.

Chorus 3
They told me you missed school today
So what I suggest you just throw them all away.
The handbags and the gladrags
That your poor old Grandad had to sweat to buy,
   ‖: A   A/G | D/F♯   E7   :‖
Oh._____

Chorus 4 As Chorus 3

Outro
| A   A/G | D/F♯   E7 |
| A   A/G | D/F♯   D/E | A

© COPYRIGHT 1967 EMI UNITED PARTNERSHIP LIMITED.
ALL RIGHTS RESERVED. INTERNATIONAL COPYRIGHT SECURED.

Introduction

This song, a hit for Stereophonics, was originally written by Mike d'Abo (one of Manfred Mann's lead singers) in 1967.

Picking Pattern

The Stereophonics recording is lead by the piano but has some nice guitar parts too. The easiest part to hear is the acoustic part, which plays some lovely arpeggiated chords, as shown below.

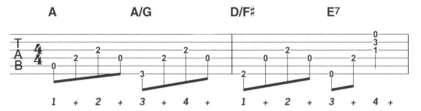

There are many variations on this pattern, but this is a good starting point. As you progress through the song you might like to add a few more frills, extra notes and flourishes—experiment and see what you find.

E7sus4

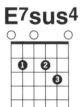

Chorus Strumming

For the chorus you should start strumming—it's very hard to hear exactly what was played because the production is so richly orchestrated, but I can hear consistent eighth-note down-strums on the acoustic guitar for sure. There are electric guitar parts here too but very low in the mix, which is filled with piano, organ, strings and oboe!

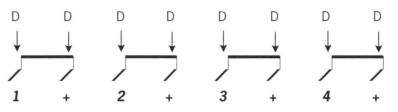

Hells Bells

Words & Music by Angus Young, Malcolm Young & Brian Johnson

Intro

riff 1 ————————————————————————————

‖: A5   Asus4   Am7 | Am7   Asus4 |

| A5   Asus4   Am7 | Am7   A7sus4   C5 G/B Am :‖ *(Play x5)*

riff 1b ————————————————————————————

| A5   Asus4   Am7 | Am7   Asus4 |

| A5   Asus4   G5 |G5 D5 C5 G/B A5 |

riff 2 ————————————————————————

‖: A5   D5 | D5 C5 G/B :‖

Verse 1

riff 2 (x4)
I'm a rollin' thunder, pourin' rain
I'm comin' on like a hurricane.
My lightnin's flashin' across the sky
You're only young but you're gonna die

Pre-chorus 1

D5 |D5   C5 G5 |
I   won't take no prisoners, won't spare no lives
D5 |D5   C5 G5 |
  Nobody's puttin' up a fight
E5 |E5   D5 A5 |
I   got my bell, I'm gonna take you to hell.
E5 |E5   (G5)
  I'm gonna get you, Satan get you.

Chorus 1

G5 |riff 1
Hell's bells, yeah hell's bells.
                riff 1b
You got me ringin' hell's bells.
My temperature's high, hell's bells.

Link 1

Play riff 2

Verse 2

I'll give you black sensations
Up and down your spine,
If you're into evil, you're a friend of mine.
See my white light flashin' as I split the night,
'Cause if good's on the left, then I'm stickin' to the right.

Pre-chorus 1

As Pre-chorus 1

Chorus 2

As Chorus 1

Solo

| A5 | A5 | A5 | A5 |

riff 3 *(Play x3)*

© COPYRIGHT 1980 J. ALBERT & SON PTY. LIMITED.
ALL RIGHTS RESERVED. INTERNATIONAL COPYRIGHT SECURED.

Solo
(cont.)

Chords as Pre-chorus 1

Chorus 3

riff 1
Hell's bells, Satan's coming to you.
Hell's bells, He's ringin' them now.

(riff 1)
Hell's bells, the temperature's high,

| C5   D5 C5 G/B A5 |
Hell's bells, a - cross the sky,   Hell's...

(riff 1)
...bells, they're takin' you down,

| C5   D5 C5 G/B A5 |
Hell's bells,   they're draggin' you down, Hells...

(riff 1)
...bells, gonna split the night,

| C   D |
Hell's bells, there's no way to fight, yeah.

Outro

riff 3 *(Play x3)*

D5 | A5 G5 A5 |
...Hell's   bells.

Introduction

This is one of the most onomatopoeic riffs of all time (look it up if you don't know what that means!), which I'm sure is playing in the elevator on the way down! It was released on one of the greatest rock albums of all time, AC/DC's *Back In Black*.

The Unsung Hero

The unsung hero of AC/DC is Angus Young's older brother Malcolm. His rhythm guitar playing is peerless and studying it will teach you a whole lot about rock guitar. Angus might have all the flash licks but without that solid groove underneath, it wouldn't rock half as hard! As with many AC/DC records, the guitars are panned and you can hear Malcolm in the left and Angus in the right speaker / headphone. Malcolm often plays technically simple parts which are surprisingly hard to perfect!

continued...

Riff 1

Riff 1 is played during the intro and the chorus, and is very simple. During the first 3 bars, use your 1st finger (fretting hand) for all the notes except the 9th fret on the third string, for which you'll use your little finger. In the 4th bar, play a two note power chord on C and then a G/B diad for which you should stretch your 1st finger back a fret.

Riff 1

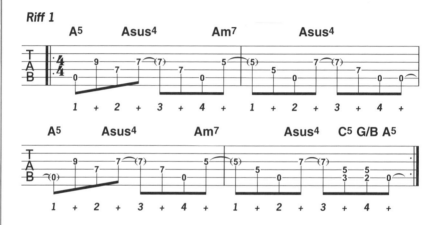

Riff 1b is a slight variation of Riff 1—the first two bars are the same, but the last two bars use open G5 and D5 chords.

Riff 1b (last 2 bars)

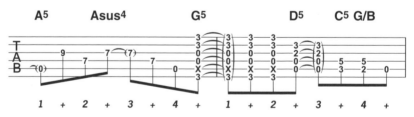

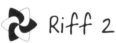 Riff 2

Riff 2 is played throughout the verses, and again is not hard to play, but make sure you play it clean and tight. I've written out both Angus and Malcolm Young's guitar parts here: although they are ver similar it's interesting to hear how well they work together—they almost sound like one huge guitar!

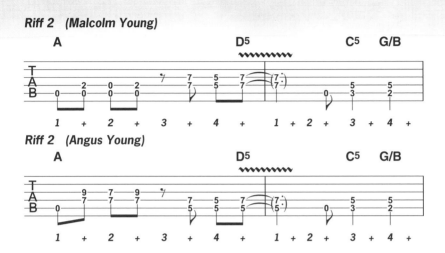

Riff 2   (Malcolm Young)

Riff 2   (Angus Young)

The pre-chorus uses simple power chords, all played as eighth-note down-strums, although Malcolm plays the chords in open position (occasionally doing a sneaky first finger lift on the D chord). The chorus mainly uses riff 1, with a couple of variations—'1b' which appears at the end of the chorus, and a very similar variation which appears in the final chorus.

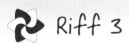 Riff 3

Riff 3 is a two-bar accompanying riff, which appears in the solo and outro.

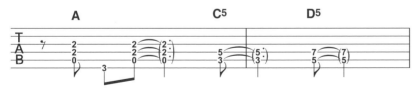

 Tone

Getting an AC/DC guitar tone is easier than you might think. The 'trick' is not adding much distortion—mostly the sound is achieved by plugging a guitar with humbucker pickups into a tube amp and turning it up loud! You may need to add some additional overdrive, but not too much.

Don't Stop Believin'

Words & Music by Steve Perry, Neal Schon & Jonathan Cain

Beginner

Intro

| E | B | C#m | A | |
| E | B | G#m | A | |

Verse 1

E   B   C#m   A
Just a small town girl livin' in a lonely world,
E   B   G#m   A
She took the midnight train goin' any - where.
E   B C#m   A
Just a city boy born and raised in south Detroit,
E   B   G#m   A
He took the midnight train goin' any - where.

Link 1

As Intro

Verse 2

A singer in a smokey room,
A smell of wine and cheap perfume.
For a smile they can share the night,
It goes on and on and on and on.

Intermediate

Chorus 1

|B/A A |B/A A6sus2 |B/E E |B/E   E
Strang - ers wait - ing,   up and down the boule - vard,
  |B/A A |B/A A6sus2 |B/E E |B/E E
Their sha - dows search - ing in the night.
|B/A A |B/A A6sus2 |B/E E |B/E   E
Street - lights peo - ple,   living just to find e - motion,
|B/A A |B/A A6sus2 |B   E |B E A |
Hid - ing some - where in the night.

Intermediate +

Link 2

| E | B | C#m | A | |

Verse 3

Working hard to get my fill, everybody wants a thrill.
Payin' anything to roll the dice just one more time.
Some will win, some will lose, some were born to sing the blues.
Oh, the movie never ends, it goes on and on and on and on.

Chorus 2

As Chorus 1

TAB

Guitar solo

| E | B | C#m | A | |
| E | B | G#m | A | |

Outro Verse

Don't stop believin', hold on to the feelin',
Streetlight people.
Don't stop believin', hold on,
Streetlight people. *(Vocals ad lib. to fade)*

© COPYRIGHT 1981 WEED HIGH NIGHTMARE MUSIC AND LACEY BOULEVARD MUSIC
ALFRED MUSIC PUBLISHING COMPANY INCORPORATED/UNIVERSAL/MCA MUSIC LIMITED.
ALL RIGHTS RESERVED. INTERNATIONAL COPYRIGHT SECURED.

Introduction

Before it became the theme song for the TV show, *Glee*, this was a hit for the rock band Journey in 1981. The song has a great guitar riff and a piano riff that translates really well to guitar.

Piano Sequence

The intro and verse sequence are both played on the piano but work really well for guitar. Of course you can just play the regular chords on the guitar, but I've also written out a fingerstyle TAB arrangement of the piano part, which will make the song instantly recognisable!

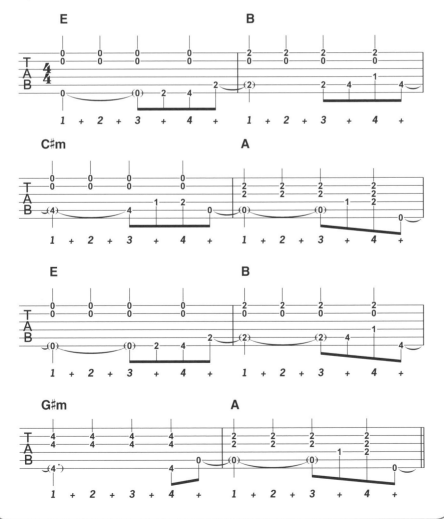

continued...

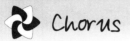
Chorus

In the chorus the guitar plays some small triad (three-note) grips right up the neck, using open strings. For the B/E and E chords, make sure you mute the 5th string with whichever finger is closest to it!

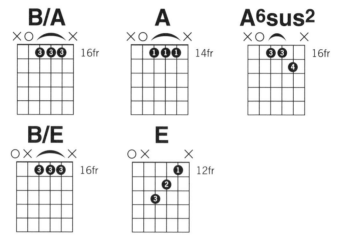

All of these chords can also be played down the octave. The E chord now becomes a standard E chord.

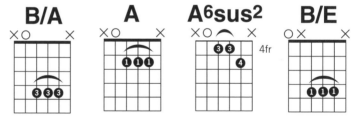

After the first chorus the guitar kicks in with a seriously cool riff!

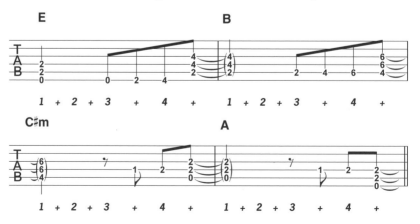

I Love Rock 'N' Roll
Words & Music by Alan Merrill & Jake Hooker

Introduction

Former Runaways guitarist Joan Jett had her greatest success with this 80s rock anthem, recorded with her band The Blackhearts.

Intro + Chorus Riff

The intro and chorus have a very recognisable riff—it's a mix of power chords and some linking bass notes and then a lead lick that reappears throughout the song. Make sure you ace this riff before trying to get through the rest of the song, which will come pretty quickly if you get this riff right. This part is played by two guitars, both of which have been transcribed below:

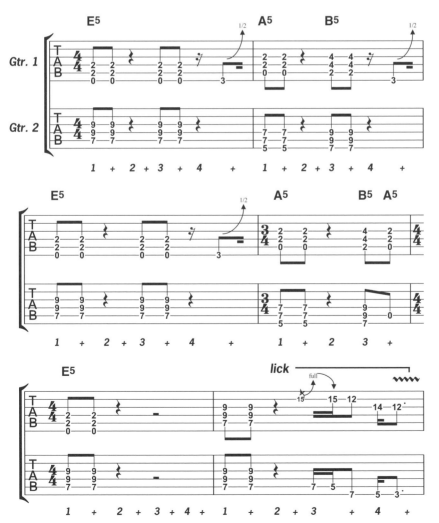

91

I Love Rock 'N' Roll

Words & Music by Alan Merrill & Jake Hooker

Beginner

Intermediate

Intermediate +

TAB

Intro

riff
| E | A B | E | 3/4 A | B 4/4 E | E lick |

Verse 1

E |E lick
I saw him dancing there by the record ma - chine,
|E |B lick
I knew he must have been about seven - teen.
    |A   B 2/4|E   4/4|A
The beat was going strong playing my favourite song.
        A   N.C.
And I could tell it wouldn't be long till he was with me, yeah me.
        N.C.
And I could tell it wouldn't be long
                B
Till he was with me, yeah me, singing:

Chorus 1

riff
I love rock 'n' roll,
So put another dime in the jukebox, baby.
I love rock 'n' roll   E |E lick |
So come on take your time and dance with me.

Verse 2

He smiled so I got up and asked for his name,
'That don't matter,' he said, ''cause it's all the same.'
I said, 'Can I take you home, where we can be alone?'
Next we were moving on and he was with me, yeah me,
Next we were moving on and he was with me, yeah me, singing:

Chorus 2

As Chorus 1

Verse 3

(Guitar Solo)
| E | E lick | E | B lick |

I said, 'Can I take you home, where we can be alone?'
Next we were moving on and he was with me, yeah me,
And we'll moving on and singing that same old song,
Yeah with me, singing:

Chorus 3

As Chorus 1 *(a capella)*

Chorus 4

E   A   B
‖: I love rock 'n' roll, So put another dime in the juke-box, baby.
E
I love rock 'n' roll
3/4|A   B
So come on take your time and dance with :‖ *Play x3*

Outro

I love rock 'n' roll, so put another dime in the juke-box, baby.
I love rock 'n' roll, so come on take your time and dance with me.

© COPYRIGHT 1975 RAK PUBLISHING LIMITED.
ALL RIGHTS RESERVED. INTERNATIONAL COPYRIGHT SECURED.

 Rhythm

For the rest of the song you will be best off learning the rhythm by listening to the recording, although I have written out one verse to help you count out the rhythms if you need to. The part below is the Guitar 2 part—it should be easy to figure out the Guitar 1 part using the chord voicings from the previous page. It's worth remembering that the lead guitar lick starts on beat 3.

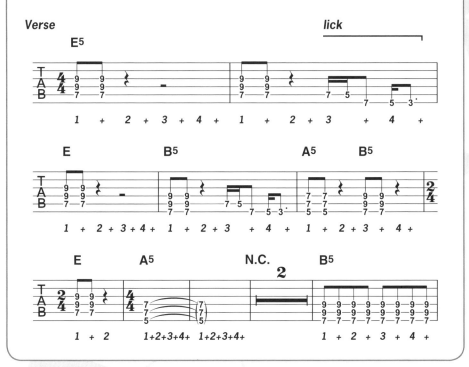

 Muting

Make sure that when you are not playing that you are covering the strings—i.e. muting by lightly touching the strings, preferably with both hands, laying your fretting fingers loosely on the fingerboard and using your outer palm to rest on the strings near the bridge.

Beginner

Intermediate

Intermediate +

TAB

Smoke On The Water

Words & Music by Ian Gillan, Ritchie Blackmore, Jon Lord, Roger Glover & Ian Paice

Beginner
Intermediate
Intermediate +
TAB

Intro

Play **riff** *(x6)*

Verse 1

G⁵   G⁵ | G⁵   F | G⁵
We all came down to Montreaux, on the lake Geneva shoreline
G⁵   G⁵ | G⁵   F⁵ | G⁵
To make records with a mobile,   we didn't have much time.
G⁵   G⁵ | G⁵   F⁵ | G⁵
Frank Zappa and the Mothers were at the best place a - round
G⁵   G⁵ | G⁵   F⁵ | G⁵
Some stupid with a flare gun, burned the place to the ground.

Chorus 1

C⁵   A♭⁵   G⁵   G⁵
Smoke, on the water,   fire in the sky.
C⁵   A♭⁵
Smoke, on the water.

Link 1

Play **riff** (x2)

Verse 2

They burned down the gamblin' house, it died with an awful sound.
The funky claude was runnin' in and out, pullin' kids out the ground.
When it was all over, we had to find another place,
Swiss time was running out, it seemed that we would lose the race.

Chorus 2

As Chorus 1

Instrumental

Play **riff** (x2)

‖: G⁵ | G⁵ | C⁵ | G⁵ | G⁵ | G⁵ | C⁵ | G⁵   :‖

| C⁵ | C⁵ | F⁵ | F⁵ |

Play **riff** (x2)

Verse 3

We ended up at the Grand Hotel, it was empty, cold and damp.
But with the rolling truck Stones thing just outside,
Making our music there.
With a few red lights, a few old beds,
We made a place to sweat,
No matter what we get out of this, I know, I know we'll never forget.

Chorus 3

As Chorus 1

Outro

Repeat **riff** *to fade*

© COPYRIGHT 1972 (RENEWED 2000) B. FELDMAN & CO. LTD. TRADING AS HEC MUSIC.
ALL RIGHTS FOR THE UNITED STATES AND CANADA CONTROLLED AND ADMINISTERED BY
GLENWOOD MUSIC CORP.
ALL RIGHTS RESERVED. INTERNATIONAL COPYRIGHT SECURED.

Introduction

This song has one of the all-time classic rock guitar riffs, and this book would not have been complete without it—it's possibly the most played riff on the guitar and it's dead easy!

Main Riff

The main riff is most commonly played using the two middle open strings, but all the live versions I have been able to find show Ritchie Blackmore playing these notes on strings 4 and 5. It turns out I've got a lot to learn myself! Another important feature of the riff is that Blackmore plays the riff using just his fingers rather than a pick—contrary to what you might expect.

Use fingers 3 and 4 (on the fretting hand) to play the notes on the 5th fret, and a small barre with finger 1 to play the notes on the 3rd fret. To play the notes on the 6th fret just move your fingers 3 and 4 up a fret. Easy!

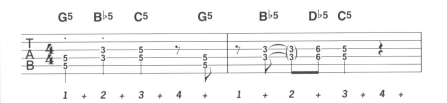

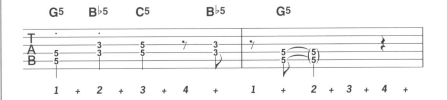

continued...

Smoke On The Water (cont.)

Verse

The verse uses a simple arpeggiated G power chord, dipping down to an F at the end of every 3rd bar, which is easy to play and sounds great when it locks in with the bass and drums.

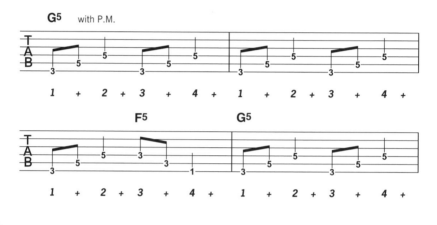

Chorus

The chorus starts with C and A♭ power chords followed initially by a kind of riff variation. There are a couple of guitars and one is just playing a big G power chord, so you could choose whether to play the riff or the chord.

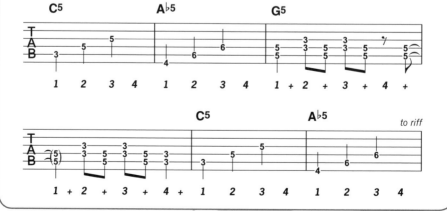

So Far Away
Words & Music by Mark Knopfler

 ## Introduction

This is Dire Straits' track from their hugely successful album *Brothers In Arms* (1985) and includes a country-style guitar riff from frontman Mark Knopfler.

Riff

The main riff played by Mark Knopfler is a great example of triad work, using small 3 note chords to create a lovely melody. There are many small variations to the riff used throughout the record—this show that they were obviously played live, not 'copy and pasted' on a computer!

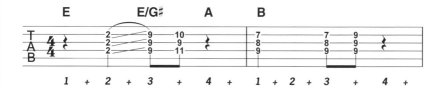

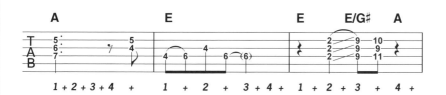

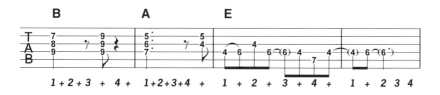

So Far Away

Words & Music by Mark Knopfler

Beginner

Intermediate

Intermediate +

TAB

Intro

| B | A | E | E E/G♯ A |

riff ___

(riff x1)

| B | A | E | E E/G♯ A |

| B | A | E | E |

Verse 1

E   E/G♯ A |B   B
Here I am again in this mean old town

                   E
And you're so far a - way from me,

  |E   E/G♯ A |B   B
And where are you   when the sun goes down?

             E
You're so far a - way from me.

Chorus 1

A   C♯m
  So far a - way from me,

B   E
  So far I just can't see,

A   C♯m
  So far a - way from me,   **(riff x1)**

B   A   E | E E/G♯ A |
  You're so far away from me.

Link 1

| B | A | E | E |

Verse 2

I'm tired of being in love and being all alone
When you're so far away from me.
I'm tired of making out on the telephone
Cause you're so far away from me.

Chorus 2

So far away from me,
So far I just can't see,
So far away from me,
You're so far away from me.

Link 2

As Link 1 *(Play x2)*

Verse 3

I get so tired when I have to explain
When you're so far away from me.
See you've been in the sun and I've been in the rain
And you're so far away from me.

Chorus 3

As Chorus 2

Link 3

(riff ad. lib)

| B | A | E | E E/G♯ A |B | A | |

© COPYRIGHT 1985 STRAITJACKET SONGS LIMITED.
UNIVERSAL MUSIC PUBLISHING LIMITED.
ALL RIGHTS IN GERMANY ADMINISTERED BY UNIVERSAL MUSIC PUBL. GMBH.
ALL RIGHTS RESERVED. INTERNATIONAL COPYRIGHT SECURED.

Beginner

```
E              |E           E/G♯ A |
You're so far a - way from me.

B         A   E          |E              E/G♯ A |
(You're so far____) Oh, you're so far away from me.
```

Coda   ‖: B | A | E | E   E/G♯ A :‖   *Ad lib. to fade*

Intermediate

🎋 Rhythm Guitar

The rhythm guitar part to this song uses 'pumping' eighth-notes and a clean electric sound, and there's an excellent lead riff interspersed with the vocal lines. Although the rhythm part might seems very straightforward at first, on closer inspection there are some tasty little fills that you can add in, like the one (see below) in the verse which uses an E/G♯ to A, climbing to the B shown below. Note that there's also a short E/G♯ 'climb' used just before the chorus.

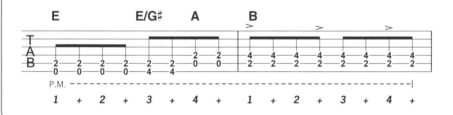

Intermediate +

🎋 Strumming

The rhythm part uses all down-strums, playing even eighth-notes with a light palm mute. This is commonly known as 'chugging' and is a very common rock and pop technique. You will rely on accents and sometimes on the pressure of the palm mute to vary the groove and dynamics between sections.

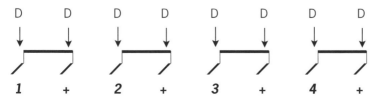

TAB

White Wedding

Words & Music by Billy Idol

Beginner

Intermediate

Intermediate +

TAB

Intro

| B5 | B5 | B5 | B5 |

riff 1 ─────────────

| Bm | Bm | E | D |

| Bm | Bm | D | E |

| Bm7 | Bm7 | Bm7 | Bm7 |

Verse 1

B5   B5   A5 E5
Hey little sister what have you done?

B5   B5   A5 E5
Hey little sister who's the only one?

B5   B5
Hey little sister who's your superman

A5   A5   B5   B5
Hey little sister who's the one you want? Hey little sister shot gun!

Chorus 1

     A5   E5   B5   B5
It's a   nice day to   start again.

     E5   D5   B5 B5
It's a   nice day for a   white wedding.

     E5   D   B5 B5
It's a   nice day to   start again.

Verse 2

w/ riff 2

Hey little sister who is it you're with?

Hey little sister what's your thoughts or wish?

Hey little sister shot gun, oh yeah

Hey little sister who's your superman? Hey little sister shot gun!

Chorus 2

(riff 2 cont.)

It's a nice day to start again.

It's a nice day for a white wedding.

It's a nice day to start again.

Link

Play **riff 2**

Play **riff 1**

Bridge

| Bm | Bm | E7(no3rd) | E7(no3rd) |

| Bm | Bm | D | E |

| Bm7 | Bm7 |

               A5 E   B5 B5
Pick it up   take me back home, yeah.

Verse 3

(riff 2)

Hey little sister what have you done?

Hey little sister who's the only one?

I've been away for so long (*so long*),

I've been away for so long (*so long*),

I let you go for so long.

© COPYRIGHT 1982 CHRYSALIS MUSIC LIMITED.
ALL RIGHTS RESERVED. INTERNATIONAL COPYRIGHT SECURED.

Chorus 3 As Chorus 2

Link 2 | B5 | B5 | B5 | B5 |

Verse 4
          B5   B5   (Bm) (Bm)
There is nothin' fair in this world
          B5   B5   B5   B5
There is nothin' safe in this world
            B5   B5
And there's nothin' sure in this world
            Bm   Bm
And there's nothin' pure in this world
          Bm   Bm   E5
Look for something left in this world ____
  D5   B5 B5
    Start again,   come on,

Outro chorus
          D5   E5   Bm Bm
It's a   nice day for a   white wedding,
        E5   D5   Bm Bm
‖: It's a   nice day to   start again,
       E5   D5   Bm Bm
It's a   nice day to   start again.   :‖ *Repeat to fade*

 # Introduction

This is Billy Idol's hit from 1982, as featured on his self-titled debut album, with guitar legend Steve Stevens playing some great riffs!

 # Riff 1

The intro, Riff 1, is played using a clean sound, letting the notes ring out and blend together.

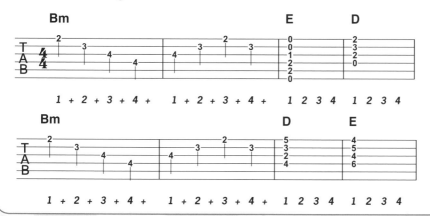

Beginner

Intermediate

Intermediate +

TAB

Rhythm Guitar

In Verse 1 the guitar pumps eighth-notes along with the bass, using a heavy palm mute but still using a pretty clean tone. Chorus 1 introduces a distorted guitar playing power chords which sustain until the next chord. There's nothing too tricky here but make sure you are muting unwanted strings or they are likely to start ringing out.

Verse 2 introduces Riff 2, a little distorted diad (two-note chord) riff that continues right through the chorus with just one stop to let the chord ring out at the end of the chorus.

Riff 2

Bridge Guitar

There are a few variations in the bridge, a few distorted 'stabs' and a variation of Riff 1, which I've transcribed below.

There is some crazy whammy bar work in Verse 4, but I'm not sure I could write it down if I wanted too, it's all about having fun with feedback, harmonics and your whammy bar!

You Do Something To Me
Words & Music by Paul Weller

 ## Introduction
This is Paul Weller's classic ballad from his acclaimed album *Stanley Road*.

 ## Piano On Guitar

The piano drives the rhythm of this song, so you have some freedom as to what rhythm you play on the guitar. One thing that you can borrow from the piano is the main riff, played in the intro and on the Em chords in the verses. Use fingers 1 and 2 to fret the Em chord and use fingers 3 and 4 to play the double stops on the thinnest two strings as shown below. It's essentially just a riff, but technically it'll make the chords Em6/9 and Emin7.

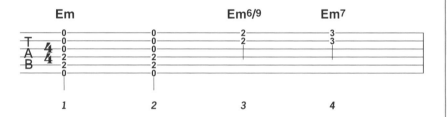

And here is another option for playing the piano riff. You can hold your 3rd finger over the third string to mute it.

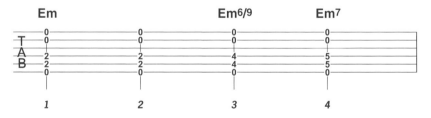

I suspect that this song was written on the piano as some of the chords are a little unusual on the guitar but more common on the piano.

C7/G

C/D

Am7

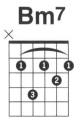
Bm7

103

You Do Something To Me

Words & Music by Paul Weller

Beginner

Intermediate

Intermediate +

TAB

Intro

| Em   Em6/9   Em7 | Em   Em6/9   Em7 |
| Em   Em6/9   Em7 | Em |

Verse 1

(Em)   D
You do something to me,
|Am7 Bm7 |Em
    Something deep inside.
Em   D
   I'm hanging on the wire,
|Am7   Bm7 |Em   Em
   For the love I'll never find.

Verse 2

You do something wonderful,
Then chase it all away.
Mixing my emotions,
That throws me back again.

Chorus 1

(Em)   C7/G
Hanging on the wire, yeah,
|Am7 C/D |Em   C7
  I'm waiting for the change,
            |G
I'm dancing through the fire,
     A7 |C   C/D | Em   Em
Just to catch a flame and feel real again.

Guitar solo

‖: D | Am7   Bm7 | Em | Em   :‖

Chorus 2

As Chorus 1

Verse 3

You do something to me, somewhere deep inside.
I'm hoping to get close to a peace I cannot find.

Chorus 3

(Em)   C7/G
Dancing through the fire, yeah,
|Am7 C/D |Em   C7
    Just to catch a flame,
      |G
Just to get close to,
    A7 |C7   C/D | Em
Just close enough to tell you that:

© COPYRIGHT 1995 SOLID BOND PRODUCTIONS LTD.
UNIVERSAL MUSIC PUBLISHING MGB LIMITED.
ALL RIGHTS RESERVED. INTERNATIONAL COPYRIGHT SECURED.

Beginner

Intermediate

Intermediate +

TAB

Verse 4

(Em)   D
You do something to me,
| Am7 Bm7 | Em   Em6/9 Em7 |
        Something deep in - side.

| Em   Em6/9 Em7 | Em   Em6/9 Em7 |
| Em   Em6/9 Em7 | Em |

Rhythm

Rhythmically I'd recommend playing all down-stroke eighth-note strumming to drive the song along, making the chords on the '+' just a light brush on the bass strings—this will really bring out the beat and groove. As usual, the best way to get the right groove will be by playing along with the record so you that pick up the rhythmic feel of the piano. You will hear a few electric guitar rhythm riffs driving things along—these should be fun to work out, and there is some lovely acoustic rhythm playing (if you listen closely) towards the end of the song.

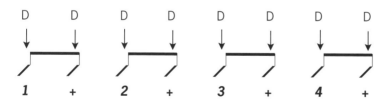

Beginner

Intermediate

Intermediate +

TAB

Introduction

Now we're going to make things a little more interesting!

It's good to keep learning new techniques and ideas, and fortunately there is a wealth of riffs and songs out there to keep you inspired. In this exciting selection, we look at songs that feature riffs, open tunings, unusual time signatures, interesting chord grips, fingerstyle patterns and a whole lot more.

With any of the more complex songs, the key to learning them well is to practise them really slowly at first. When I teach private lessons I see—time and time again—students attempting to play songs too fast, too early on in their practice. See the 'Practice Tips' at the front of this book for a structured guide on practising more advanced material.

Beginner

Intermediate + Stage:
Your Notes

Intermediate

Intermediate +

TAB

Alive

Words by Eddie Vedder, Music by Stone Gossard

Beginner
Intermediate
Intermediate +
TAB

Intro

riff

‖: **(A)**   **(Asus⁴)** | **(A)**   **(Asus⁴)** :‖

(cont. riff)   *Let ring*

‖: **A**   **Asus⁴** | **A**   **Asus⁴** :‖ ²⁄₄ **F   G   C** ⁴⁄₄ |**(C)** |

riff (x4)

Verse 1

'Son,' she said, 'Have I got a little story for you.
What you thought was your daddy was nothing but a...
While you were sitting home alone at age thirteen,
Your real daddy was dying.

              | **F**   **G C**
Sorry you didn't see him

     Cadd⁹ C | **F**   **G C**
But I'm   glad we talked.'

Chorus 1

|**E   G** |**D**   **A**
Oh, I...oh, I'm still alive.

|**E   G** |**D**   **A**
Hey, I...oh, I'm still a - live.

|**E   G** |**D**   **A** |**B**
Hey, I...oh, I'm still a - live, hey, oh.

Verse 2

Oh, she walks slowly across a young man's room.
She said, 'I'm ready for you.'
Well I can't remember anything to this very day...
'Cept the look. The look.
Oh, you know where.
Now I can't see, I just stare.

Chorus 2

|**E**   **G** |**D**   **A**
(stare...) I'm still a - live.

|**E G** |**D**   **A**
Oh, I...oh, I'm still a - live.

|**E G** |**D**   **A**
Hey, I...oh, I'm still a - live.

|**E G** |**D**   **A** |
Hey, I...oh, I'm still a - live, hey, oh.

Instr. 1

|**B** |**F♯**   ‖: ⁷⁄₈ **B** ⁴⁄₄ **F♯** :‖ *(Play x3)*

Bridge

|**A⁷ Asus² Dsus²** | **A⁷ Asus² D⁵**
     'Is something wrong?' she said.

| **A⁷**   **Asus²** **Dsus²**
Of course there is.

© COPYRIGHT 1991 WRITE TREATAGE MUSIC/INNOCENT BYSTANDER MUSIC, USA.
UNIVERSAL MUSIC PUBLISHING LIMITED/KOBALT MUSIC PUBLISHING LIMITED.
ALL RIGHTS RESERVED. INTERNATIONAL COPYRIGHT SECURED.

| | | A7 Asus2 | D5 |

(cont.)

'You're still a - live,' she said.

| B7 | Bsus2

Oh, and do I de - serve to be?

Esus2 | B7 Bsus2 E6sus2

  Is that the question?

| B7 Bsus2 | Esus2 | B7 Bsus2

And if so, if   so, who answers?

E6sus2 |

Who answers?

Chorus 3   As Chorus 2

Solo   ‖: E G | D A :‖ E |

(Play x18)

Introduction

This was the first single release by Pearl Jam, one of the greatest rock bands to emerge from the Seattle music scene of the 1990s. Their 'sound' relies on the combination of two guitars, so the rhythm parts are often as important as the lead one, and they often blend into one.

The Intro / Verse Riff

The main riff is an all-time classic and very recognisable. It's also quite unusual—it's not hard to play but takes a bit of work to get the slide and the open string hammers-ons to feel and sound smooth and to sit in the groove. You only need fingers 1 and 3, so other than keeping it tidy (and not letting unwanted strings ring out) the biggest challenge will be making sure the bend is in tune!

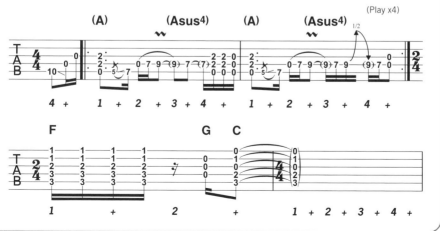

Beginner · Intermediate · Intermediate + · TAB

continued...

109

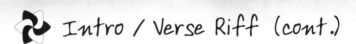

Intro / Verse Riff (cont.)

It's worth noting that in the verses you will need to back off your volume a little (back to maybe 6 or 7), which will give you a cleaner sound. If you listen to the recording you will hear that the riff is played a little softer and more rhythmically than it is in the intro.

The rhythm guitar under the riff is a clean strumming part, which makes a very interesting blend with the distorted electric guitar.

Chorus Riff

When we reach the chorus, the rhythm guitar kicks the distortion on and pumps out some big open chords, while the lead guitar swaps between chords and lead lines. This creates an exciting blend of tones, as well as great energy and a countermelody to the main vocal part (shown below).

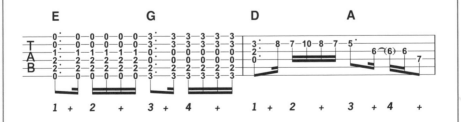

 The Bridge

The Bridge also has some very interesting guitar interplay between the very 'clean' electric guitar part and the slightly crunchy one—both parts experiment with a few different chord grips to create melody lines within the chords, which makes for an intricate texture. Below is an amalgamation of the two guitar parts:

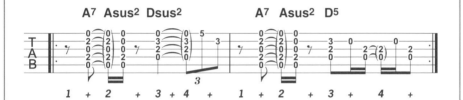

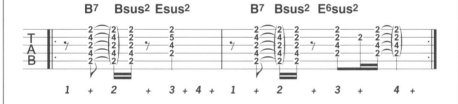

All My Life

Words & Music by Dave Grohl, Taylor Hawkins, Nate Mendel & Chris Shiflett

Beginner

Intermediate

Intermediate +

TAB

Intro

riff 1 ⌐
‖: **G5** :‖ *(Play x4)*

Verse 1

w/riff 1
All my life I've been searching for something,
Something never comes never leads to nothing,
Nothing satisfies but I'm getting close,
Closer to the prize at the end of the rope.
All night long I dream of the day
When it comes around then it's taken away,
Leaves me with the feeling that I feel the most,
Feel it come to life when I see your ghost.

Link 1

‖: **Gm** | **Gm** **Am** | **Gm** | **Gm** **B♭m** :‖

Verse 2

w/riff 2
Calm down don't you resist,
You have such a delicate wrist,
And if I give it a twist,
Something to hold when I lose my grip,
Will I find something in that?
To give me just what I need,
Another reason to bleed,
One by one hidden up my sleeve,
riff 1
One by one hidden up my sleeve.

Chorus 1

E♭   **E♭**
Hey don't let it go to waste
G5   **G5**
  I love it but I hate the taste
C/E   **F**   **B♭**
Weight keep pinning me down.   *(Play Chorus x2)*

Link 2

As Link 1

Verse 3

Will I find a believer?
Another one who believes,
Another one to deceive,
Over and over down on my knees.
If I get any closer,
And if you open up wide,
And if you let me inside,
On and on I got nothing to hide,
riff 1
On and on I got nothing to hide.

Chorus 2

As Chorus 1

© COPYRIGHT 2002 FLYING EARFORM MUSIC/LIVING UNDER A ROCK MUSIC/
I LOVE THE PUNK ROCK MUSIC/MJ TWELVE MUSIC.
UNIVERSAL MUSIC PUBLISHING LIMITED/KOBALT MUSIC PUBLISHING LIMITED/
WARNER/CHAPPELL NORTH AMERICA LIMITED.
ALL RIGHTS RESERVED. INTERNATIONAL COPYRIGHT SECURED.

Link 3	| Gm	| Gm	Am	| Gm	| Gm	B♭m |
	riff 1 (x4)					

Verse 4 — As Verse 1

Bridge 1
w/riff 1
(And I'm) Done, done, and I'm onto the next one   (x8)
G5   G5
Done, done, and I'm onto the next one   (x8)

Link 4
riff 1 (x4)

Bridge 2
w/riff 1
Done, done, onto the next one,
Done I'm done and I'm onto the next one
Done, done, onto the next one,
Done I'm done and I'm onto the next.

Chorus 3 — As Chorus 1

Link 5
riff 1 (x2)

Outro
w/riff 1
Done, done and onto the next one
Done I'm done and I'm onto the next.

 ## Introduction

Dave Grohl really should not be allowed to have so much talent—it's not fair on the rest of us! But at least we get to enjoy Foo Fighters' high energy rock, as this song demonstrates.

Riff 1

The song starts with a fat power chord pumping away on G5, and you can really feel the storm brewing! To keep it tight during the rests, make sure you take the pressure off the chord, but don't remove you fingers completely—just relax the grip, and the chord will stop as the strings will be muted.

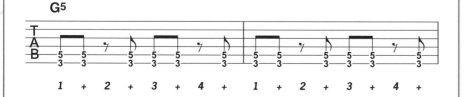

113

Beginner

Intermediate

Intermediate +

TAB

 Riff 2

Now we kick into an awesome rock riff, where the notes are not too tricky but the rhythm has to be tight—this should take you some practice and listening. As usual you should start by listening to the song a number of times so that you really have the sound in your ears, I'd also recommend using a software slow-downer (like *Transcribe!* or *Audacity*) so you can practise the rhythm at a slower speed, maybe at 60% of the original speed.

You should only start playing this riff once you are sure you know how the riff goes. Use fingers 2 and 3 to fret the notes—the 1st finger will sit behind and mute the strings. Be aware that Foo Fighters are a two guitar band, so your guitar will sound 'thinner' than the recording, especially as Foo Fighters recordings usually include quite a few layers, building up a huge wall of guitars!

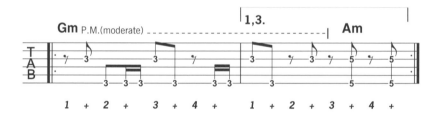

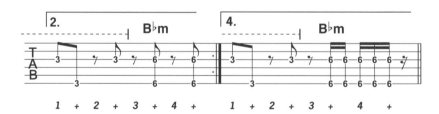

 Chorus

The Chorus has some lovely chords in it—they use interesting grips that sound great with a high-gain rock guitar sound. Check out some live clips and you'll see that Grohl is playing these chord grips while Chris Shiflett rocks out some power chords behind.

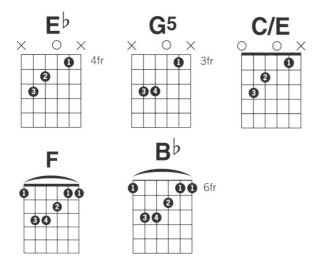

To really nail this song you will have to take these different components and then learn the form of the song by listening and playing along. This song has a complex form but the individual bits are not so complicated. You'll have to put in some effort to play them well, but it'll be totally worth the effort.

All Right Now

Words & Music by Paul Rodgers & Andy Fraser

Beginner

Intermediate

Intermediate +

TAB

riff

Intro ‖: A5 D/A │ A5 │ Dadd11 D │ A5 :‖ *(Play x4)*

Woah, woah woah!

Verse 1
There she stood in the street,
Smiling from her head to her feet
I said, 'Hey, what is this now, baby?'
Maybe, maybe she's in need of a kiss.
I said, 'Hey, what's your name, baby?
Maybe we can see things the same.
Now don't you wait or hesitate,
Let's move before they raise the parking rate.'

Chorus 1
| A5 | G5 | | D/F# | A5 | |
All right   now, baby it's-a all right now.
| A5 | G5 | | D/F# | A5 | A5 |
All right   now, baby it's-a all right now.

Link Play **riff**

Verse 2
I took her home to my place,
Watchin' ev'ry move on her face.
She said, 'Look, what's your game, baby?
Are you tryin' to put me in shame?'
Baby, I said-a, 'Slow, don't go so fast.
Don't you think that love can last?'
She said, 'Love, Lord above,
Now you're tryin' to trick me in love.'

Chorus 2
| A5 | G5 | | D/F# | A5 |
All right   now, baby it's-a all right now.
| | G5 | | D/F# | A5 |
All right   now, baby it's-a all right now.

Instrumental ‖: A5 │ G5 D │ A5 │ G5 D :‖ *(Play x8)*

│ E5 │ E5 │

Chorus 3
| A5 | G5 | | D/F# | A5 |
‖: All right   now, baby it's-a all right now.
| A5 | G5 | | D/F# | A5 |
All right   now, baby it's-a all right now. :‖ *Repeat to fade*

© COPYRIGHT 1970 BLUE MOUNTAIN MUSIC LIMITED.
ALL RIGHTS RESERVED. INTERNATIONAL COPYRIGHT SECURED.

Introduction

Rock guitar doesn't get much better that this, although there is a lot of debate surrounding exactly how to play the main riff. I'm going to give you my take on it, which I believe to be correct, but without having witnessed the recording session, we'll never know for sure! Please bear in mind that this lesson is based on the shorter 'single' edit of the song, relased by Free in 1970, not the full album version.

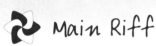

Main Riff

This is one of the most recognisable riffs in rock and a sure-fire classic. The first thing to note is that the there are a number of different versions of this song—some with surprisingly different mixes of the main riff. There are two guitars playing on the studio recording, so what we have below is a summary of the two parts.

The second thing to note is that the guitar is not as distorted as you might think—it sounds to me more like a very loud amp that is 'breaking up' than a distortion pedal. You also need to listen closely to the riff and try to pick up the subtle textures in it—the loud and soft, the notes that are barely there, the groove in the rhythm—these are the things that will really make the riff sound right.

The first chord 'move' starts with you playing the A as a mini-barre using your first finger, with your little finger forming a mini-barre on the 5th fret of the thinnest two strings. Then remove your little finger and place fingers 2 and 3 down to form the D/A—this is an all-time classic rock move, used by The Rolling Stones and many other massive bands of the 60s and 70s.

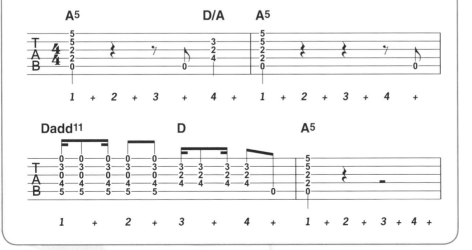

Beginner

Intermediate

Intermediate +

TAB

117

 ## Chorus

The chorus sounds best played with the exact voicings—sure, you could use other chord grips (and in a 2-guitar band it would certainly be worth exploring) but to play 'just like the record', follow the TAB and directions shown below.

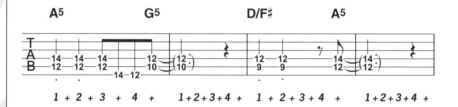

 ## Solo Section

The solo section is great fun to jam over—just let rip with your blues licks, based on the A Minor Pentatonic, and you'll have a ball. It's a great solo to work out on your own, especially if you're using software to slow the song down, in which case you shouldn't find it hard at all, and it'll be very satisfying to figure it out. Good luck!

Back In Black

Words & Music by Angus Young, Malcolm Young & Brian Johnson

Introduction

This is one of the greatest and best-loved rock tunes of all time, written and recorded by AC/DC, one of the biggest-selling bands of all time, on their album *Back In Black* (1980).

Riff 1

This is 'the one'—If you learn only one rock guitar riff in your life, make it this one! We start with some easy open power chords—for the D and A, I suggest you use DUD strums as I've seen Malcolm and Angus Young doing that on video, but it won't matter if you use all down-strums.

Then we have a lead line based on the E Minor Pentatonic scale; the rhythm is important here, so notice that the first note is on the second sixteenth-note. Listen and count along, observing which notes fall on the beat (tap your foot and nod your head on the beat).

After playing the open power chords again we have another lead riff, with a tricky rhythm—it's easiest here is to listen to the track until you really know it, but I've written the count under it too if you prefer to do it that way.

Riff 1

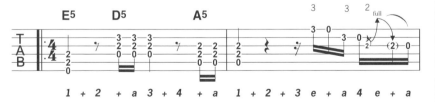

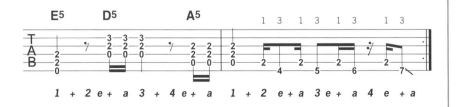

Back In Black

Words & Music by Angus Young, Malcolm Young & Brian Johnson

Beginner

Intermediate

Intermediate +

TAB

Intro

riff 1

‖: E5 D5 A5 | A5 | E5 D5 A5 | A5 :‖

Verse 1

riff x4
Back in black, I hit the sack,
I've been too long, I'm glad to be back.
Yes, I'm let loose from the noose
That's kept me hangin' about.
I keep lookin' at the sky
'Cause it's gettin' me high.
Forget the hearse 'cause I'll never die.
I got nine lives, cat's eyes,
Abusin' ev'ry one of them and runnin' wild.

Chorus 1

riff 2
'Cause I'm back, yes I'm back.
riff 3
Well I'm back, yes I'm back.
riff 2
Well I'm back, back
        G   D
Well I'm back in black, yes, I'm back in black.

Verse 2

Back in the back of a Cadillac,
Number one with a bullet, I'm a power pack.
Yes, I'm in a bang with the gang,
They gotta catch me if they want me to hang.
'Cause I'm back on the track,
And I'm beatin' the flack.
Nobody's gonna get me on another rap.
So, look at me now, I'm just a-makin' my play,
Don't try to push your luck, just get outta my way.

Chorus 2

As Chorus 1

Guitar solo

‖: E5 D5 A/C♯ | A/C♯ E5 | E5 D5 A/C♯ | A/C♯ E5 A5 E5 A5 :‖
(Play x4)

Chorus 3

As Chorus 1

Bridge

| E5 | E5 | E5 | E5 | A5 | A5 | E5 | E5 |

Chorus 4

As Chorus 1

Guitar solo

Let ring

A5   (A5)   ‖: E5 D5 A/C♯ | A/C♯ E5 |

| E5 D5 A/C♯ | A/C♯ E5 A5 E5 A5 :‖ *Repeat to fade*

© COPYRIGHT 1980 J. ALBERT & SON PTY. LIMITED.
ALL RIGHTS RESERVED. INTERNATIONAL COPYRIGHT SECURED.

120

Riffs 2 + 3

These two riffs make up the chorus and you'll play: Riff 2; Riff 3; Riff 2; followed by three strums on G and three strums on D.

The tricky part here is playing the rhythm tight with the right strumming and with no rogue strings ringing out. Most rhythm figures played by AC/DC are played using down-strums on the beats and on the '+'s, and up-strums on the 'e' and 'a', which might seem counterintuitive at first, but will feel natural once you get into it. This strumming pattern will really help you lock in—watch some live videos and you'll see both Angus and Malcolm playing that way!

The rhythm here is a little tricky and the best tactic is to do a lot of listening, but counting is Ok if you have to. Watch out for the little quarter-note bend too—you'll be using your 2nd finger to reach over for it and give the note a little 'tweak', as it's not a proper bend.

Riff 2

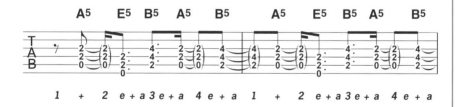

Riff 3

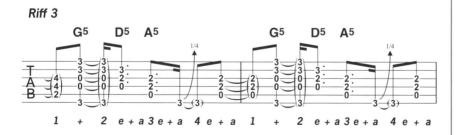

Beginner

Intermediate

Intermediate +

TAB

 ## Solo Section (Rhythm Guitar)

The next fun bit to check out is the rhythm guitar part under the solo. Malcolm Young is probably the finest rock rhythm guitar player in history so make sure you keep an ear out for his rock solid, understated and brilliant playing on other AC/DC songs. Usually the two guitars are panned separately to the left and right speakers, so you should be able to hear it pretty clearly on most songs.

This part (below) is not inherently difficult but you have to make it rock solid, sitting right in the groove with the drums and bass. Just because it's simple doesn't mean it's easy!

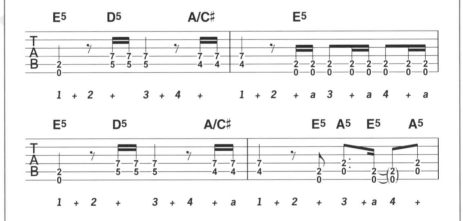

Beginner

Intermediate

Intermediate +

TAB

 Bridge Riff

Now we have a tasty little riff—this song is full of great stuff, isn't it? Follow the notes carefully here, as it will make all the difference. It might seem hard at first with all the jumping around the fretboard but it sounds awesome once you get it, and I'm showing you the part here exactly as Angus plays it.

Try to nail the riff in E first and then move it all down a string to the A string and get that cooking. Then you will go back to the riff in E before jumping right into Riff 2, which can feel like a strange transition, but if you've got all the pieces right you shouldn't find it takes too much practice…and after that, you'll have learnt whole song!

Black Hole Sun

Words & Music by Chris Cornell

Intro

| Gsus4 | B♭6/9 | F5 | | E5 | | E♭sus4 | D7(no3) | | D7(no3) | |

Verse 1

(D7)   G6   B♭6
In my eyes, indisposed,

      F5   Em
In disguise as no one knows,

       E♭   Dsus4
Hide the face, lies the snake,

  G6   G/F   A♭
The sun in my dis - grace.

Verse 2

Boiling heat, summer stench,
'Neath the black the sky looks dead.
Call my name through the cream
And I'll hear you scream again.

Chorus 1

N.C.   E♭sus4   D7(no3)
Black hole sun won't you come

  G5   G5/F   B♭
And wash away the rain?

          E♭sus4   D7(no3)
Black hole sun won't you come,

    C   Csus4   C   D   D
Won't you come?   Won't you come?

Verse 3

Stuttering, cold and damp,
Steal the warm wind, tired friend.
Times are gone for honest men
And sometimes far too long for snakes.

Verse 4

In my shoes, a walking sleep,
And my youth I pray to keep.
Heaven send hell away,
No one sings like you anymore.

Chorus 2

Black hole sun won't you come
And wash away the rain?
Black hole sun won't you come,

    C   Csus4   C   B♭5
Won't you come?
Black hole sun won't you come
And wash away the rain?
Black hole sun won't you come,

    ‖:C Csus4 C |B♭5 |D5   :‖ (Play x4)
Won't you   come?   (Won't you..)

© COPYRIGHT 1994 YOU MAKE ME SICK I MAKE MUSIC
UNIVERSAL/MCA MUSIC LIMITED
ALL RIGHTS RESERVED. INTERNATIONAL COPYRIGHT SECURED

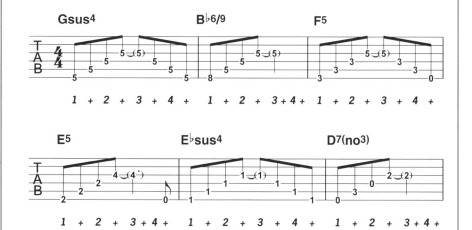

Instrumental	‖: $\frac{9}{4}$ **D5**　　　　**G/F5**　　:‖ *(Play x6)*
	$\frac{4}{4}$ **F5**　**G5** │ **G5**　│
Verse 5	Hang my head, drown my fear 'Til you all just disappear.
Chorus 3	As Chorus 2...
	‖: **C**　**Csus4**　**C** │ **B♭5** │ **D5**　　　　:‖ *(Play x8)* ...won't you come?　　　　(Won't you
Instrumental	$\frac{9}{4}$ **D5**　　　　**G/F5**　│
	$\frac{4}{4}$ **F5**　　　**G5**　│

Introduction

This song by Soundgarden is amazing, and if you dig the tune you should look up the solo acoustic version performed by Chris Cornell for *Yahoo! Music*—it's super awesome! This song is in drop D and the original recording seems a little sped up, making it a little sharp.

Intro Riff

The main riff requires some strong barres but fingering should be pretty logical—take your time and get it right slowly before trying to play along. Remember that all guitars have the thickest string tuned down to D.

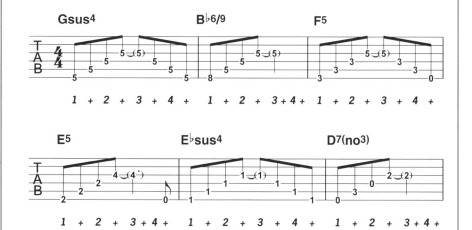

continued...

Beginner

Intermediate

Intermediate +

TAB

Beginner

Intermediate

Intermediate +

Verse Lead Guitar

The verse chord sequence is almost identical to the intro but adds a couple of bars. Next up we're going to check out the verse lead guitar part because it's so cool! The rhythm is similar to the intro guitar part that we've just played, but it is played higher up the neck with some heavy effects (chorus, delay and a Leslie speaker). Find a fingering that is comfortable for you.

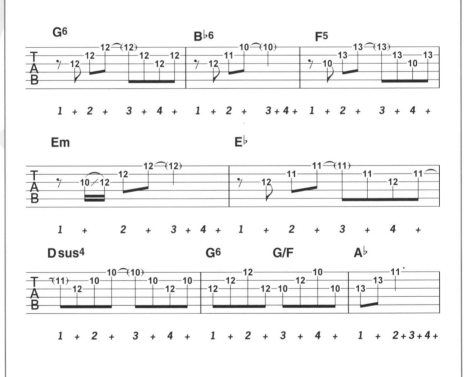

TAB

Beginner

Intermediate

Intermediate +

TAB

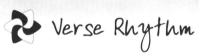 Verse Rhythm

Below is a transcription of the rhythm pattern used when Chris Cornell performs this song solo. I should point out that this exact part isn't played on the album version of the song, but will probably be your best bet if you're playing solo.

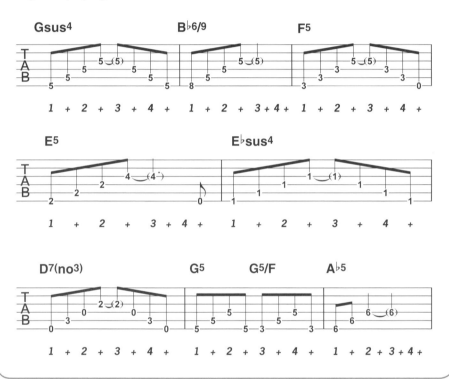

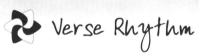 Chorus Guitar

The Chorus uses similar chords to the verse but with some variations at the end. It's nothing too tricky but make sure you have a good listen to the original recording to make sure you have the rhythm correct and that it's grooving!

continued...

127

Beginner

Intermediate

Intermediate +

TAB

Chorus

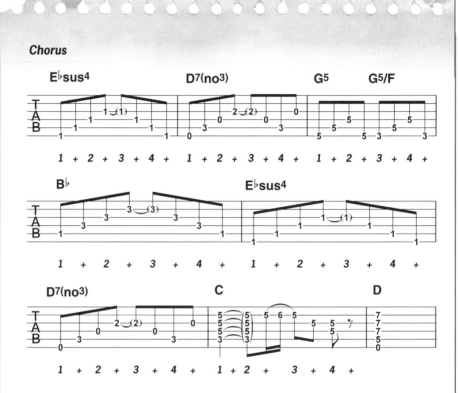

♫ Instrumental / Outro Riff

The last part I'm giving you for this song is the crazy 9/4 riff (it's probably 4/4 and then 5/4 but I'm trying to keep it understandable) that plays in the instrumental section. It's tricky to play in such a strange time signature—9 beats to the bar—but with some listening and slow practice you'll crack it.

These are all the components to the song, but if you listen to the recording you will hear some slight variations which I haven't given you. However, you have all you need! I expect you to listen to the original recording as well as learning the written parts, and if you do both, it will become obvious when there is a slight chord change at the end of a verse, because you will have played that change somewhere else!

Just The Way I'm Feeling

Words & Music by Grant Nicholas

 ## Introduction

This is a fantastic song by the underrated Welsh rockers Feeder. It's a really catchy track with some lovely guitar parts.

 ## Chords

These chord grips form one of the main features of this song. All the chords hold down the note D (second string, fret 3) and the note A (third string, fret 2), which creates an interesting drone effect. When coupled with the intricate sixteenth-note strumming pattern, they create a distinctive sound.

Layers

There are many guitar layers in this song. It's hard to define them exactly but you might like to work them out on your own by looping the main chord sequence and then experimenting by picking out the notes D, A, and maybe the occasional C# at various points on the neck. Listen closely and try to find some of the patterns used on the record— you'll learn a lot experimenting this way!

Also note that there are big power chords in the chorus, so if you are playing it on your own you might like to kick in distortion at that point and give it some welly!

129

Just The Way I'm Feeling

Words & Music by Grant Nicholas

Intro

riff ──────────────────────────────

| Bm7 | (Bm7) D5/A Gsus2 |

Verse 1

riff x8

Love in, love out, find the feeling.
Scream in, scream out, time for healing.
You feel the moments gone too soon,
You're watching clouds come over you.

Pre-chorus 1

D/F♯   Gsus2   Bm7   Gsus2
   Torn in two,   you close your eyes for some place new,

D/F♯   Gsus2
   Torn in two.

Chorus 1

| Asus4   Bm7 | Gsus2
   And I feel it's going down,

     D/F♯ | Asus4
Ten feet below the ground,

     Bm7 | Gsus2
I'm waiting for your healing hand,

     D5 | Asus4
One touch could bring me round,

     Bm7 | Gsus2
I feel we're going down,

     D/F♯ | Asus4
Ten feet below the ground,

     Bm7 | Gsus2   D5 |
It's just the way I'm feeling.

Link 1

Play **riff x2**

Verse 1

Glow in, burn out, lost the feeling.
Bruise in, you bruise out, nurse the bleeding.

Pre-chorus 2

Torn in two,
Each time we bruise.

Chorus 2

As Chorus 1

| Asus4   Bm7 | Gsus2   D/F♯ |
...yeah, yeah, it's just the way I'm feeling.

Bridge

| Bm7   Asus4 | Gsus2
   Two different views,

       | Asus4   Bm7 | Gsus2
As words confuse   and   break.

© COPYRIGHT 2002 UNIVERSAL MUSIC PUBLISHING LIMITED.
ALL RIGHTS RESERVED. INTERNATIONAL COPYRIGHT SECURED.

(cont.)	|Bm7 Asus4 | Gsus2
	I can't get out,
	D/F♯ |E7sus4 D/F♯ |Gsus2
	There's no way out of here,
	|Asus4 Bm7 | Gsus2
	I can't get clear.
Link 2	Play **riff x2**
Verse 3	Love in, love out, find the feeling.
Chorus 4	As Chorus 2
	...yeah, yeah, it's just the way I'm feeling. (x4)

 Rhythm

The rhythm is important here, and the main (verse) sequence has some interesting features, mainly that the chord changes in the 2nd bar happen on the 2nd sixteenth-note and not on the beat. Because these are played with an up-strum, you don't hear the bass note change very clearly (and that's the only bit that's changing). However, making the chord change alters the feel of the rhythm—you lose the expected heavy down hit on the beat so it has an almost syncopated feel. Very tasty!

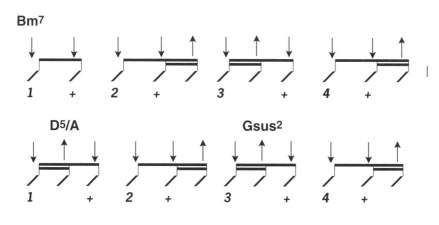

Hole Hearted

Words & Music by Nuno Bettencourt & Gary Cherone

Intro

riff 1 ─────────────────────────

‖: D   E/D | E/D   :‖ *(Play x3)*

| D   E/D   F/D | F/D |

riff 2 ──────────────────────────────────

‖: A⁷ | A⁷ | A⁷   D | C   G/B   G   A :‖

Verse 1

w/riff 2 (x2)
Life's ambitions occupy my time
Priorities confuse the mind.
Happiness one step behind
This inner peace I've yet to find.

Pre-chorus 1

|D   A/D | G/D   A/D*   D
Rivers flow in - to   the   sea,

    |A⁷   D/A |A⁷(no⁵)   D/A   A⁷
Yet even the sea is not so full   of   me.

 |D   A/D | G/D   A/D*   D
If I'm not blind, why can't   I   see

    |A⁷   D/A |A⁷(no⁵)   D/A   A⁷
That a circle can't fit where a square   should be?

Chorus 1

       G   Cadd⁹ |D   E/D |D   E/D |
There's a hole in my heart that can only be filled by you.

       G   Cadd⁹ |D   E/D
And this hole in my heart can't be filled with the things I do.

     riff 3 ─────────
    |Fsus²   C/E   C |D   E/D | riff 3
Hole hearted,   hole hearted.

Link

Play **riff 2**

Verse 2

This heart of stone is where I hide,
These feet of clay, kept warm inside.
Day by day less satisfied.
Not fade away before I die.

Pre-chorus 2

As Pre-chorus 1

Chorus 2

There's a hole in my heart that can only be filled by you.
And this hole in my heart can't be

Cadd⁹ |D   A/D*   G/D*   D |
filled with the things I do.

© COPYRIGHT 1990 ALMO MUSIC CORPORATION/COLOR ME BLIND MUSIC, USA.
RONDOR MUSIC (LONDON) LIMITED.
ALL RIGHTS IN GERMANY ADMINISTERED BY RONDOR MUSIKVERLAG GMBH.
ALL RIGHTS RESERVED. INTERNATIONAL COPYRIGHT SECURED

Beginner

Chorus 3   There's a hole in my heart that can only be filled by you.
Should've known from the start I'd fall short with the things I do

|D E/D |riff 3 |D E/D

(do.)   Hole hearted, *(hole hearted)*

|riff 3 |D   E/D

Hole hearted, *(hole hearted)*

|riff 3 |D   E/D |riff 3 |D

Hole hearted, hole hearted.

 Introduction

This song was a hit for Extreme in 1991. It's a great song to play on a 12-string guitar but it works fine on a 6-string too. Nuno Bettencourt is an incredible guitar player and his clever guitar parts sound really impressive. Note that if you are playing along with the original recording, you'll need to tune your guitar down a semitone (use your tuner: $E\flat$, $A\flat$, $D\flat$, $G\flat$, $B\flat$, $E\flat$).

 Riff 1

The sequence of chords during the opening riff is simply a D chord moved up a few frets, with some notes picked. A similar idea is used later in the pre-chorus and chorus. It's not hard to play but you want to make sure that you settle well into the groove and play at the right tempo. Make sure you use the right strumming and keep the (strumming) hand moving.

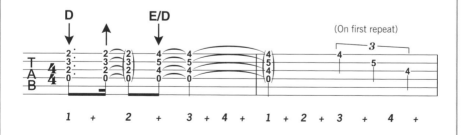

Beginner

Intermediate

Intermediate +

TAB

continued....

Beginner

Intermediate

Intermediate +

TAB

 Riff 2

This is the main riff for the song and the most recognisable bit. It's got a few tricky little flick-offs, which are barely audible on the recording but getting them in there really makes the part sound like the recording.

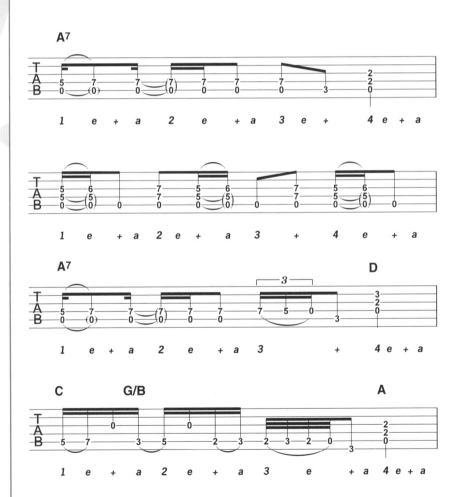

Beginner

Intermediate

Intermediate +

TAB

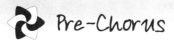

Pre-Chorus

We're looking at triads (three-note chords) over bass notes here. The first five chords uses triad grips on the thinnest 3 strings, with the open D string ringing out. The last three chords use shapes on strings 2 and 4, with an open A in the bass.

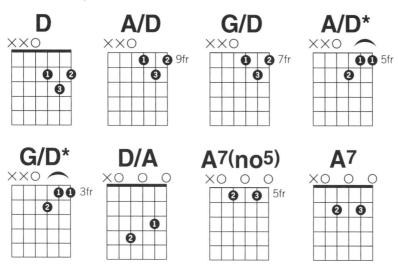

Chorus

The chorus is a mix of strumming and picking out notes individually—it also uses the seemingly ubiquitous Cadd9 which was found in almost every 90's hair metal acoustic song! The only real tricky bit is the last few bars with the little flick-offs, which can be a little tricky. Again, the big issue is making sure you get the rhythms right, and the best way to do that is by playing along with the original recording at a slower speed (using software).

Riff 3

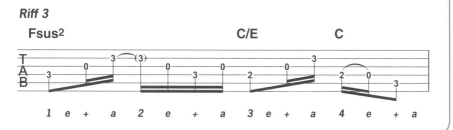

135

Iris

Words & Music by John Rzeznik

Intro

$\frac{4}{4}$ ‖: Bm | Bm(add9) | G5 | Gmaj7 :‖

Verse 1

$\frac{6}{8}$ D5   D5/E | G5*
And I'd give up for - ever to touch you,
| D5/B   D5/A | G5*
'Cause I know that you feel me some - how.
| D5   D5/E | G5*
You're the closest to heaven that I'll ever be
| D5/B   D5/A | G5*
And I don't want to go home right now.

Verse 2

And all I can taste is this moment,
And all I can breathe is your life.
And sooner or later it's over,
I just don't want to miss you tonight.

Chorus 1

(G5) | Bm   Bm(add9) | G5
And I don't want the world to   see me,
| Bm   Bm(add9) | G5
'Cause I don't think that they'd under - stand.
| Bm   Bm(add9) | G5
When everything's made to be broken,
| Bm   Bm(add9) | G5
I just want you to know who I am.

Link 1

$\frac{4}{4}$ | Bm | Bm(add9) | G5 | Gmaj7 |
| Bm | Bm(add9) $\frac{6}{8}$ | G5   Gmaj7 |

Verse 3

And you can't fight the tears that ain't coming,
Or the moment of truth in your lies.
When everything feels like the movies,
Yeah, you bleed just to know you're alive.

Chorus 2

As Chorus 1

Verse 4

Instrumental

Interlude

$\frac{4}{4}$ ‖: Bm | Bm(add9) | G5 | Gmaj7 :‖ (Play x3)

| Bm | Bm(add9) |

| G | G | D/F♯ | D/F♯ |

| G | G | D5/B | D5/B |

| G | G | D/F♯ | D/F♯ |

© COPYRIGHT 1998 SCRAP METAL MUSIC.
EMI VIRGIN MUSIC LIMITED.
ALL RIGHTS RESERVED. INTERNATIONAL COPYRIGHT SECURED.

(cont.)		D5/B		D5/B		D5/B	D5/C♯*	D5*		D5/E*	D5*	D5*/C♯*

	G		G		D/F♯		D/F♯	

	D5/B		D5/B		D5/B	D5/A	G5*		D5/F♯	D5/E	D5	

6/8 ‖: D5/B* | D5/C♯ | D5 | D5 | |

	D5/B		D5/A		G5*		G5*	:‖

Chorus 3 As Chorus 1

Chorus 4 As Chorus 1
...I just want you to know who I am. *(x4)*

Outro ‖: D5/B* | D5/C♯ | D5 | D5 | |

	D5/B		D5/A		G5*		G5*	:‖ *Repeat and fade*

Introduction

This song was a worldwide smash hit for the Goo Goo Dolls in 1998 and it features a crazy, unique tuning.

Cautionary Note

Before we get going I should point out that as well as the main guitar part that I'm teaching you, there are a lot of other guitars, mandolins and maybe even a banjo in the mix, so don't expect your one guitar to conjure up the whole record. I'll get you as close as I can to the main acoustic guitar part, but this is as much an exercise in how far you can take re-tuning and exploring the instrument as it is in learning the song itself.

continued...

Beginner

Intermediate

Intermediate +

TAB

 Tuning

To play this song authentically you need to do some serious re-tuning of the guitar. It's quite a pain to carry out, but the good news is that it's the hardest part of playing the song—once you've re-tuned, the rest is pretty simple.

⑥ = B (lower)   ③ = D (lower)

⑤ = D (lower)   ② = D (higher)

④ = D (same)   ① = D (lower)

The biggest problem with detuning the strings this much is that they get very floppy and will rattle on the frets—not a great sound! The worst offenders here are the thickest two strings, so if you are recording this tune, I'd recommend that when you re-tune, you replace these two strings with thicker strings—which you'll have to buy especially for the thickest string: something like a .60 or .70 gauge.

Chords

Once you've got the tuning sorted, let's look at the chord grips. You'll see that most of them are very simple and that the verse in particular is a doddle, and just involves moving one note around on the thickest string; it doesn't get much easier than that!

Beginner

Intermediate

Intermediate +

TAB

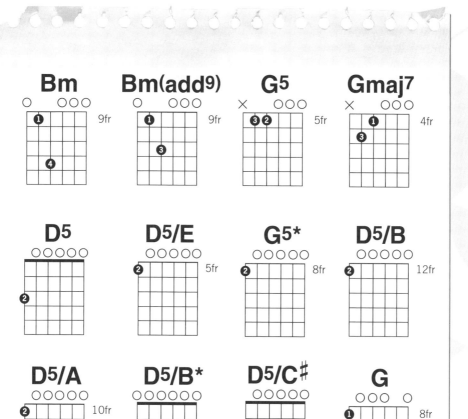

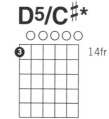

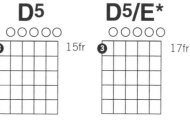

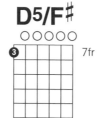

Rhythm

Once you've learnt all of the chords, it's time to look at the two main rhythm patterns: one for the 4/4 sections and one for the 6/8 sections. Getting the pattern solid is pretty important and will really make the song sound 'just like the record' if you've gone to the trouble of the crazy re-tuning.

Intro / Link 1

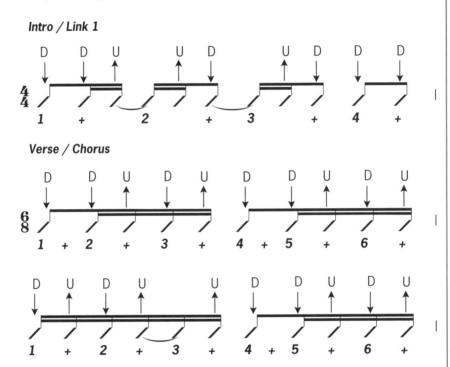

Verse / Chorus

Interlude

Now the interlude…what do we do about that? The original has a million overdubs of strings, electric guitar, slide and a host of other pads to fatten it up, so on one lone acoustic guitar it will sound pretty thin by comparison! I've left the chords in there for you in case you want to have a crack at it with your band, but if you're playing this song solo, you will probably want either to leave this section out or to shorten it right down. Notating all the rhythms would be so complicated to read as to make it futile, so if you want to crack this section you just have to get your ears on it!

Beginner

Intermediate

Intermediate +

TAB

Where Is My Mind
Words & Music by Black Francis

Introduction

This classic Pixies alt-rock song is pretty easy to play and has a great, simple guitar riff and is a good barre chord workout!

Strumming

It's the strumming and a few little tweaks that make the pattern for this song recognisable. All the chords are barre chords except for the open E chord at the start of the main sequence.

Follow the strumming pattern carefully; you'll need to listen to the recording to pick up the groove and dynamics properly. Here are some pointers to check out:

1. The up-strum before each chord change is either muted or will include open strings ringing out while the chords change.

2. To play the A chord, start by just holding the barre down with your first finger, then put fingers 2/3/4 down in the usual place for the next two strums (the e +), lift the shape up again and leave the barre for the 'a', with the shape back down for the '4 e' and then lift off the chord altogether and strum the open strings for the last two strums.

Complicated? Not if you use your ears, listen closely, and practise slowly.

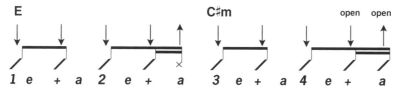

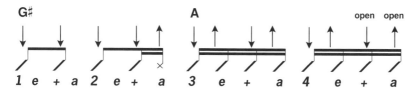

There are a few variations to the pattern, such as the obvious 'long hold' where you just let the chord ring out—if you listen you'll pick up these variations in no time.

Where Is My Mind

Words & Music by Black Francis

Intro

```
‖: E    C#m  | G#    A    :‖
   riff ─────────────────────────
‖: E    C#m  | G#    A    :‖
```

Verse 1

riff x3
With your feet on the air and your head on the ground,
Try this trick and spin it, yeah.
Your head will collapse
If there's nothing in it and you'll ask yourself...

Chorus 1

```
|E              C#m  |
   Where is my mind?
|G#             A    |
  Where is my mind?
        |E      C#m      | G#   A  |
Where__ is my     mind?

|E        C#m  | G#     A      |
                         (Way...)
        |E     G#   | A       Am      |
Way__ out__ in the water, see it swimming.

| C#m      | B          |
```

Verse 2

I was swimming in the Caribbean,
Animals were hiding behind the rocks
Except the little fish.
But they told me, he swears, trying to talk to me, coy koi.

Chorus 2

As Chorus 1

Instr.

```
| B     | B     | B       |
```

Verse 3

As Verse 1

Chorus 3

As Chorus 1

Outro

riff x7
Ooh.
With your feet on the air and your head on the ground,
Try this trick and spin it, yeah.
Ooh.

UNIVERSAL/MCA MUSIC LIMITED.
ALL RIGHTS RESERVED. INTERNATIONAL COPYRIGHT SECURED.

✿ Strumming (cont.)

If you would rather have a more precise, notated version of the main strumming pattern, here is a TAB of it below:

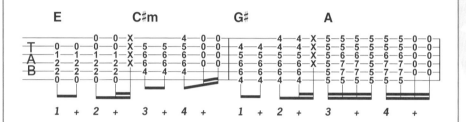

✿ Lead Riff

There is also a very easy and cool lead riff that appears in various points in the song, it's tabbed below. There's nothing tricky in there—just using fingers 1 and 2, with a small barre on the 4th fret for the G♯ chord.

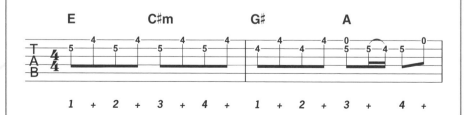

Killing In The Name

Words & Music by Tim Commerford, Tom Morello, Brad Wilk & Zack De La Rocha

Intro

| D5 | D5 | D5 | D5 |

| D E♭ | D E♭ | D E♭ | D E♭ |

riff 1 ⌐————————————————————⌐

‖: D E♭ | D E♭ | D E♭ | D E♭ :‖

riff 2 ⌐——⌐

| D E♭ | D E♭ | D E♭ | D E♭ |

Killing in the name of...

Link

riff 3 ⌐——⌐

‖: D7   :‖ *(Play x4)*

Verse 1

w/riff 3 (x8)
Some of those that work forces,
Are the same that burn crosses   *(x4)*

Pre-chorus 1

riff 4
Ugh! Killing in the name of.
riff 4   **C5**
     Killing in the name of.

riff 5
  Now you do what they told ya. *(Play x12)*

Chorus 1

riff 6 (x8)
Those who died are justified,
For wearing the badge, they're the chosen whites
You justify those that died
By wearing the badge, they're the chosen whites   *(Play x2)*

Verse 2   As Verse 1

Pre-chorus 1   As Pre-chorus 1

Chorus 2   As Chorus 1

Guitar Solo   Play **riff 6**

Bridge | D5 | *(x8)*

Outro

w/riff 6 (x16)
F*** you, I won't do what you tell me! *(x16)*
Motherf***er!

play **riff 6 (x4)**
| D5 | D5 E♭5 |

© COPYRIGHT 1992 RETRIBUTION MUSIC.
WIXEN MUSIC UK LTD.
ALL RIGHTS RESERVED. INTERNATIONAL COPYRIGHT SECURED.

Introduction

This is my personal favourite Christmas No. 1! It's a big song, and had a big impact on my generation. The song is by Rage Against The Machine, whose name itself is a strong message.

Drop-D Tuning

Lets start at the top shall we? We're in drop-D tuning and the song starts with some big sustained open D5 power chords ringing out. That stops and the bass takes over.

When the guitar comes back in we're playing this funky riff with some low D notes and a higher lead line.

Riff 1

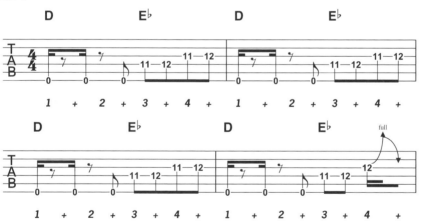

After four repeats we reach a unsion riff with the bass:

Riff 2

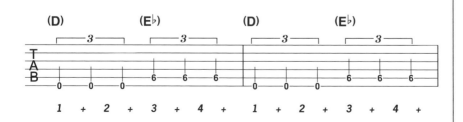

Beginner

Intermediate

Intermediate +

TAB

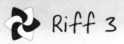

Now we're getting down to business with this masterpiece of a funk rock riff! Be aware of the dynamics changing when the vocal comes in—bring it down and play a little softer but keep the same energy if you can. We have to keep it funky but relaxed.

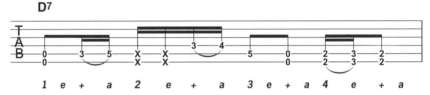

In the break we have another great funky riff, similar to the last riff but with a descending top note. Remember that when playing power chords in Drop-D tuning (like at the end of this riff), you can just barre your finger flat across the thickest three strings.

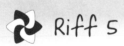

Now we have the 'stops' part. Learn just the pitched notes first, keeping quiet between the notes, and once you are confident with that you can start adding in the muted hits like the ones you'll hear on the record. Make sure you keep it free and funky—the groove is king here!

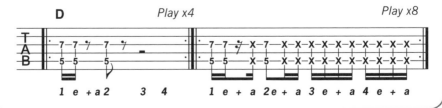

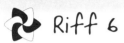

Riff 6

In the chorus we have a riff mixed in with some power chords, helping to bring the energy up a notch.

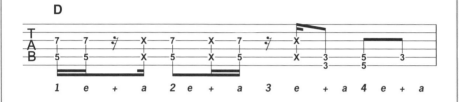

Verse Variation

In the next verse have a couple of cool variations like this little scale run (which is a killer to remember when playing it live, especially if you're bouncing around the stage energetically!).

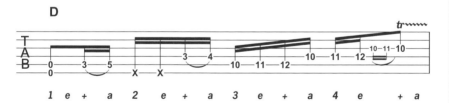

Solo

The solo in this song introduced the 'Whammy' pedal, a very cool toy now made by Digitech, to the world. You'll never replicate the solo without one, although if you get hold of one you'll find you can get recreate the vibe pretty easily. Either way, play around with the solo and have some fun with it!

Other than a few extra bits, like the free improvisation just after the solo section (labelled Bridge), we've now got all the parts covered.

147

My Sharona

Words & Music by Douglas Fieger & Berton Averre

Drums | **4** **Bass** | **4**

Intro
riff 1
| G5 | G5 | G5 | C B♭ |

Verse 1
riff 1 (x2)
Ooh my little pretty one, pretty one,
When you gonna give me some time, Sharona?
Will you make my motor run, my motor run,
Honey coming off of the line, Sharona?

Pre-chorus 1
G5   G5
Never gonna stop, give it up, such a dirty mind,
 B♭   B♭
I always get it up for the touch of the younger kind.
|C   E♭|E♭   F |
My my, my my my, wooh!

Chorus 1
riff 1
M-m-m-my Sharona.

Verse 2
Come a little closer, huh, be a hon,
Close enough to look in my eyes, Sharona.
Keep a bit of mystery, get to me,
Running down the length of my thigh, Sharona.

Pre-chorus 2 As Pre-chorus 1

Chorus 2
G5   G5   G5   G5
M-m-m-my Sharona,   m-m-m-my Sharona.

Guitar solo 1
lick   (Play x3)
‖: Csus4 C   E♭9 | E♭5 F E♭ F | G5 | G5 :‖
lick
| Csus4 C   E♭9 | E♭5 F E♭ F | D | D |

Link 1 Play riff 1 (x2)

Verse 3
When you gonna give to me, give to me;
Is it just a matter of time, Sharona?
Here's a trip to destiny, to destiny,
Or is it just a game in my mind, Sharona?

Pre-chorus 3 As Pre-chorus 1

Chorus 3
G5   G5   C   E♭   F
M-m-m-m-m-m-m, my-my-my-my-my wooh!

© COPYRIGHT 1979 SMALL HILL MUSIC/EIGHTIES MUSIC/WISE BROTHERS MUSIC LLC.
REACH GLOBAL (UK) LIMITED/CHESTER MUSIC LIMITED TRADING AS CAMPBELL CONNELLY & CO.
ALL RIGHTS RESERVED. INTERNATIONAL COPYRIGHT SECURED.

Beginner

Intermediate

Intermediate +

TAB

	G5	G5	G5	G5

Chorus 4   M-m-m-my Sharona,   m-m-m-my Sharona. *(Play x2)*

Link 2 |C G/C | F/C   G/C | C G/C | F/C   G/C |

Guitar solo 2   ‖: C   G | F   G | C   G | F   G :‖ *(Play x5)*

| C   G | F   G | D | D | N.C. |

Link 3   ‖: G5 | G5 | G5 | G5 :‖

w/riff 1

Coda   ‖:   Oh, my Sharona! :‖   *(Play x3)*

Introduction

This is one of the most enjoyable songs to play on the guitar (ever!) and I think that every young band should have a go at it. It's got a few tricky bits, but on the whole, you should focus on mastering the main riff and getting the whole band sounding tight.

Riff 1

This is the real focus, a very cool riff using octaves and some slides. The big deal here is making sure you keep all the other strings muted, so use the outside of finger 1 to mute all the strings under it. The chord part after the octave riff is a barre chord on C, lifting off finger 3—this is not hard but may take some practice to get it sounding clean, and to get all the notes ringing out clearly.

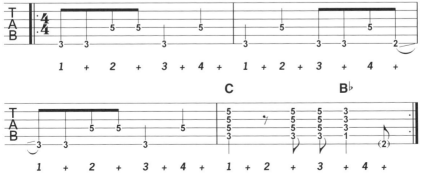

continued...

149

Beginner

Intermediate

Intermediate +

TAB

Pre-Chorus Guitar

The pre-chorus uses power chords and pumping eighth-notes—but have a good listen to the rhythm being played. The second guitar part continues playing octaves with the bass part, which sounds great.

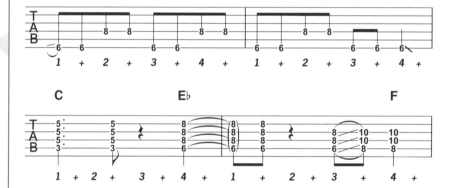

Link 2

In link 2 you will see some slash chords, but be aware that while the bass is playing the note C, the guitar is just playing triads on strings 2/3/4 of C (xx555x), G (xx543x) and F (xx321x).

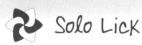 Solo Lick

There are two guitar parts in the first solo section. The first is a chord-based riff which is really cool, and will take a fair bit of practice to get the rhythms right.

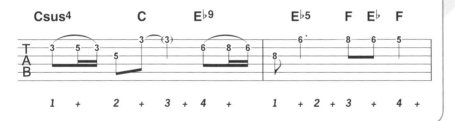

The second part is a lead guitar playing licks from the C Minor Pentatonic scale and picking out chord tones. Below is the catchy lick played by the lead guitar which forms the 'hook' of this solo section.

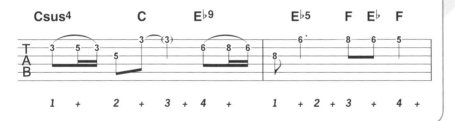

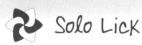 Guitar Solo 2

The second solo section is over a completely new chord sequence. The lead guitar will now will be playing from the C Major Pentatonic (same notes as A Minor Pentatonic) as the band rocks the new chords underneath it. There is a cracking guitar solo on the original recording that you might like to check out too!

Run To The Hills

Words & Music by Steve Harris

Beginner

Intermediate

Intermediate +

TAB

Intro

Drums

|———— 4 ————|

riff 1 ————————————————————————————————————

|A5   D5 |D5   A5 |C5   D5 |G5   A5 |

Verse 1

w/riff 1

White man came across the sea
He brought us pain and misery
He killed our tribes he killed our creed
He took our game for his own need.
We fought him hard we fought him well
Out on the plains we gave him hell
But many came too much for Cree
|C5   D5 |G5   D5 |D5   D5 |
Oh will we ever be set free?

Verse 2

D5   D5
Riding through dustclouds and barren wastes
C5 |C5   G/B C5 G/B |
Galloping hard on the plains
D5   D5
Chasing the redskins back to their holes
C5 |C5   G/B C5 G/B |
Fighting them at their own game
A5   C5
Murder for freedom a stab in the back
F5   D5   D5
Women and children and cowards attack.

Chorus 1

G5   G5   F5   F5
   Run to the hills
C5 |C5   G/B |G5   G5
   Run for   your lives.
G5   G5   F5   F5
Run to the hills
C5 |C5   G/B |G5   G5
   Run for   your lives.

Verse 3

Soldier blue on the barren wastes
Hunting and killing's a game,
Raping the women and wasting the men
The only good Indians are tame.
Selling them whisky and taking their gold
Enslaving the young and destroying the old.

Chorus 2

As Chorus 1

© COPYRIGHT 1982 IMAGEM MUSIC.
ALL RIGHTS RESERVED. INTERNATIONAL COPYRIGHT SECURED

Guitar Solo	‖: E5	| G5	| C5	| C5	:‖	*(Play x4)*
	‖: A5	| B5/A	| C5/A	| D5/A	:‖	*(Play x4)*

Chorus 3	As Chorus 1 *(Play x2)*

Introduction

Up the Irons! This is one of the most famous songs by Iron Maiden—a proper heavy metal band—with all the spandex and harmony guitar solos you can take!

Riff 1

This main riff has two distinct guitar parts: one plays a kind of two-note riff over a drone bass note, while a lead part plays wailing bends. You can play either part, or get a looper pedal going and do both! For the rhythm part, I tend to use fingers 1 and 4 for the power chord shapes and a barre with my 1st finger for the others, except the D in the 3rd bar, for which I use fingers 3 and 4. These are by no means your only options, so you should experiment with the fingering and see what works best.

The big deal with the lead part is making sure it's in tune! Plenty of bending practice is required to master all the jumping around and bending notes.

Rhythm Part

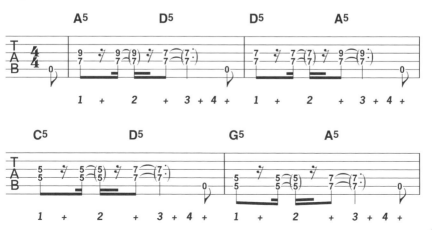

Riff 1 (cont.)

Lead Part

Rhythm

There are some complex and demanding rhythmic figures in this song, interspersed with breaks, where you will play sustained chords, giving your picking hand a brief rest!

In the verses you will be playing a palm-muted 'galloping' rhythm of D DU which at this speed takes some stamina! Make sure you accent the note on the beat—usually the DU at the end is just the root note, while for the chord on the beat you should push through it to play both notes of the power chord.

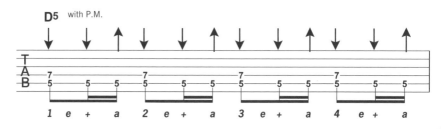

Beginner

Intermediate

Intermediate +

TAB

 Moving On

After the gallop on the D and C chords you have the C to G/B section, where each chord will just be played once, giving you a quick breather for the muscle to recover before galloping off again! Make sure you just move finger 1 back a fret for the G/B—for this reason you might like to play the D5 and C5 with fingers 1 and 4.

At the end of the verse the chords are sustained, although one of the guitars is putting some extra hits in there, so you can play it by ear and see how you feel it.

Chorus

The chorus moves between sustained chords, the gallop and another metal rhythm trick used on the F chord (after the lyric 'hills')— D DU D with the final down-strum being sustained—like a mini gallop but holding the chord at the end. It's obvious if you listen to it, but I've written the pattern below, nonetheless.

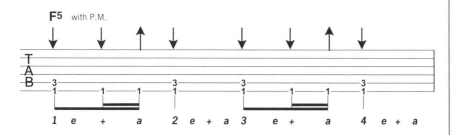

Since You've Been Gone

Words & Music by Russ Ballard

Beginner

Intermediate

Intermediate +

TAB

(riff variation)

Intro | G5 D5 | E5 C5 | G5 D5 E5 | C5 D5 | D5 |

Verse 1

| G   D/F♯ |
I get the same old dreams,
| Em   Dsus2 |
Same time every night
| C   G/B | A7   Dsus2 |
Fall to the ground and I wake up,
| G   D/F♯
So I get out of bed,
  | Em   Dsus2 |
Put on my shoes and in my head,
| C   G/B | A7   Dsus2 |
Thoughts right back to the break-up.

Pre-chorus 1

E♭5   F
These four walls are closing in
E♭5 | Am   D |
Look at the fix you've put me in.

Chorus 1

w/riff (x3)
Since you've been gone,
Since you've been gone,
I'm out of my head can't take it.
Could I be wrong,
But since you've been gone
You cast a spell, so break it.
Woah-oh, woah-oh, woah-oh
Since you've been gone.

Verse 2

So in the night I stand
Beneath the back street light
I read the words that you sent to me.
I can take the afternoon
But night-time comes around too soon
You can't know what you mean to me.

Pre-chorus 2

Your poison letter, your telegram
Just goes to show you don't give a damn.

Chorus 2 As Chorus 1

Instrumental | G   Am7 | G/B C | G/D B | Em Em/D | C Am |

© COPYRIGHT 1976 RUSSELL BALLARD LIMITED.
COMPLETE MUSIC LIMITED.
ALL RIGHTS RESERVED. INTERNATIONAL COPYRIGHT SECURED.

Beginner

Bridge

```
|G    Am7    |G/B
If you will come back
C        |G/D         B      |Em    Em/D |C   Am  |D      |
Baby, you know you'll never do wrong _____
```

Chorus 3

```
|A                      E |F♯m                      D
Since you've been gone,    Since you've been gone,
    |A          E  |F♯m D   E   |
I'm out of my head can't take it.
Could I be wrong,
But since you've been gone,
You cast a spell, so break it.
|A        E/G♯ |F♯m        F  |A/E      E    |F♯m        F  |
Woah-oh,      oh - oh,        oh - oh,   oh - oh,
|A/E      E         |A    A
Ever since you've been gone.
```

Instrumental ‖: A   E |F♯m D |A   E F♯m |D   E   :‖

Outro chorus Repeat Chorus *(to fade)*

Intermediate

 # Introduction

This huge and perennial hit from Rainbow came out in 1979, but is still found on radio playlists around the world. The main riff is an all-time guitar classic and is great fun to play.

The Main Riff

The main riff is instantly recognisable but often played incorrectly; most commonly it is played with all power chords, but a close listen will reveal that the first G chord is an open power chord. Once you've got the chords right you just need to make sure the rhythm is tight, and ensure you use your picking hand's outer palm to mute all the strings between chords, making sure you are using all down-strums.

There are a couple of minor variations to the riff at the transition points into sections—I'll leave you to work these out on your own, as all you have to do is listen!

After the Bridge, you will have to move this whole sequence up a tone (2 frets) which will require playing the first chord (now A) as a power chord instead of open, but the rhythm will remain the same.

Intermediate +

TAB

continued... 157

The Main Riff

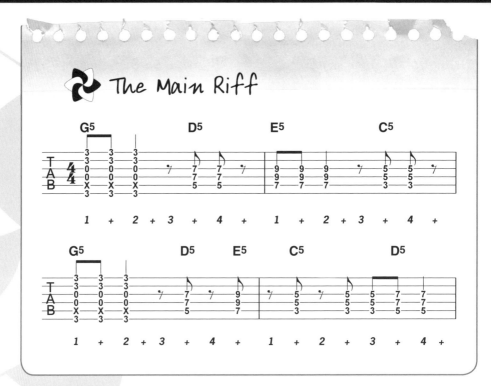

Verses

For the verses we have an arpeggiated chord sequence. It's quite a specific pattern but you are free to experiment and pick out different notes. I'd suggest starting with either the picking pattern D D D U or D U D U on each chord, and then taking it from there.

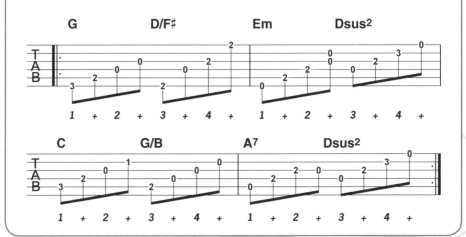

Pre-Chorus

In the pre-chorus we have a very cool little lead line—it's nothing too tricky but what is important is the rhythm! You can either listen to the track repeatedly until you know how it goes, or you can count out the rhythm as shown under the TAB. Do it very slowly and then gradually build up the speed in either case.

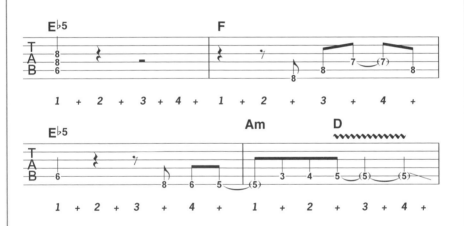

159

Beginner

Intermediate

Intermediate +

TAB

 Bridge

Probably the trickiest part of the song is the bridge, where there are lots of chord changes and a lead line. You could play either, preferably the chords if you are playing on your own or the lead line if you are jamming it with a band.

Lead Part

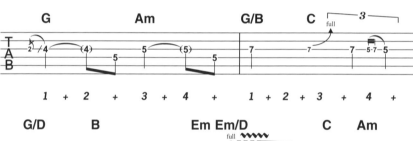

Rhythm Part

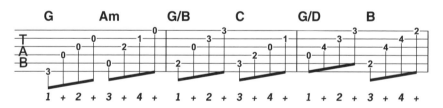

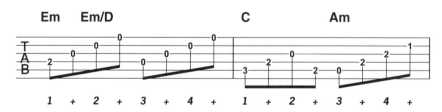

Steady, As She Goes
Words & Music by Jack White & Brendan Benson

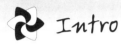

Introduction

Jack White and Brendan Benson rocked it up with this track by their supergroup The Raconteurs, on the album *Broken Boy Soldiers* (2006).

Intro

Most of this song uses the same four chords, so the different sections of the song have to be identified by the changes to the texture. The intro has a simple lead line with a tasty vibrato as shown below.

Riff

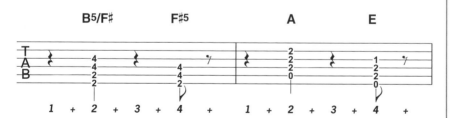

Then the guitar starts with short stabs, playing the chords once each, on beats 2 and 4—make sure you keep them tight by relaxing the chord grip after you have played it and using the picking hand to rest on the string too. Especially at a louder volume, muting between stabs is very important.

After playing twice through a 'push' is added, moving the chords that were on beat 4 a half beat early, which adds loads of energy.

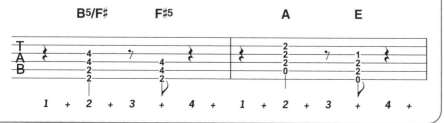

161

Steady, As She Goes

Words & Music by Jack White & Brendan Benson

Beginner

Intermediate

Intermediate +

TAB

> ### Sequence for Verse & Chorus
> ‖: Bm F♯ | A E :‖

Intro

Drums | Bass
4 | 4

Play **riff (x2)**

Play Sequence x2

Verse 1
Find yourself a girl and settle down,
Live a simple life in a quiet town.

Chorus 1
Steady as she goes, *(steady as she goes.)*
Steady as she goes, *(steady as she goes.)*
So steady as she goes.

Verse 2
Your friends have shown a kink in the single life.
You've had too much to think, now you need a wife.

Chorus 2
Steady as she goes, *(steady as she goes.)*
Steady as she goes, *(steady as she goes.)*

Bridge 1
   (E)   G5
Well here we go a - gain,
             A   B5
You've found your - self a friend that knows you well.
| B5   A | G5
  But no matter what you do,
           A   E5   E5
You'll always feel as though you tripped and fell.
So steady as she goes.
(Play Sequence x2)

Verse 3
When you have completed what you thought you had to do,
And your blood's depleted to the point of stable glue.
Then you'll get along.
Then you'll get along.

Play **riff (x1)**

Chorus 3
As Chorus 2

Bridge 2
As Bridge 1

© COPYRIGHT 2006 THIRD STRING TUNES, CHRYSALIS MUSIC AND GLADSAD MUSIC
ALL RIGHTS FOR THIRD STRING TUNES CONTROLLED AND ADMINISTERED BY EMI MUSIC PUBLISHING LTD
ALL RIGHTS FOR CHRYSALIS MUSIC AND GLADSAD MUSIC CONTROLLED AND ADMINISTERED BY
CHRYSALIS MUSIC GROUP, INC., A BMG CHRYSALIS COMPANY
ALL RIGHTS RESERVED. INTERNATIONAL COPYRIGHT SECURED

Verse 4   Settle for a girl, neither up or down.
Sell it to the crowd that is gathered round.
Settle for a girl, neither up or down.
Sell it to the crowd that is gathered round.

Play **riff (x2)**

Chorus 4   As Chorus 2 *(Play x2)*

Outro   Steady as she goes, *(are you steady now?)* *(Play x4)*
Steady as she goes.

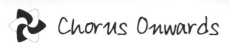

Chorus Onwards

When the song breaks into the chorus, there is another level of
distortion; either a pedal is added, or the guitar volume has been turned
down a bit for the verses and then cranked up for the chorus—both
have a similar effect. You'll really want to give it some force too, so play
it hard and give it lots of energy, letting all the chords ring out. Listen to
the original recording and try to emulate some of the vibe—this kind of
track is more about vibe and feel than anything else!

The Bridge introduces the only variation to the chord sequence, but it's
simple enough to play—just keep pumping away at the chords with
lots of gain, and be aware of the half bars on the B and A which might
catch you out if you aren't expecting them.

Later in the song there are more and more variations on the main riff
where small muted strums are added in, kicking the energy up another
notch. You are best off listening to the track and trying to find them
by experimenting, but I've written one out for you (below) to get you
started, as most of what is played is similar to this:

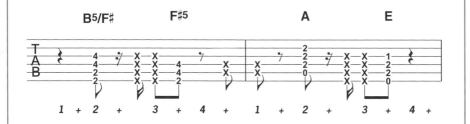

Sweet Leaf

Words & Music by Terence Butler, John Osbourne, Frank Iommi & William Ward

Intro

riff 1

‖: **A5** **D5** **C♯5** | **C5**   **D5** :‖ *(Play x6)*

Alright now,
Won't you listen?

Verse 1

w/riff 1 (x8)
When I first met you, didn't realise,
I can't forget you for your surprise.
You introduced me to my mind,
And left me wanting, you and your kind, oh yeah.

Link 1

riff 2

‖: **A5** | **G5** **C5** | **E5** **A5** | **A5** :‖ *(Play x4)*

Chorus 1

w/riff 1 (x6)
I love you,
Oh, you know it

Verse 2

My life was empty,
Forever on a down,
Until you took me, showed me around.
My life is free now, my life is clear,
I love you sweet leaf, though you can't hear, oh yeah.

Link 2

Play **riff 2** *(x4)*

Interlude

| **A5** | **A5** | **A5** | **A5** |

‖: **B5** | **B5** | (**B5**) **C♯5** | **C♯5** :‖

| **B5** | **B5** | (**B5**) **C♯5** |

Guitar solo

C♯5	**C♯5**	**C♯5**	**C♯5**
C♯5 **B5**	**C♯5** **B5**	**C♯5** **B5**	**C♯5** **B5**
C♯5	**C♯5**
C♯5	**C♯5**	**C♯5**	**C♯5**
C♯5	**C♯5**	**C♯5**	**C♯5**

‖: **C♯5** **A5** **G♯5** **G5** | **G5** :‖ *(Play x3)* | **G5** |

Chorus 2

w/riff 1 (x6)
Come on now,
Try it out.

© COPYRIGHT 1971 WESTMINSTER MUSIC LIMITED.
ALL RIGHTS RESERVED. INTERNATIONAL COPYRIGHT SECURED.

Beginner

Intermediate

Intermediate +

TAB

w/riff 1 (x8)

Verse 3

Straight people don't know
What you're about,
They put you down and shut you out.
You gave to me a new belief,
And soon the world will love you sweet leaf.
Oh yeah, baby.

Link 3

Play **riff 2** *(x2)*

w/riff 1 (x12)

Chorus 3

Come on now, oh yeah, oh yeah.
Try me out baby.
Oh, won't you try the sweet leaf, oh yeah.
Alright, yeah, yeah, yeah.

Introduction

This classic Black Sabbath song was written about Ozzy Osbourne's favourite 'herb'. The original recording is played on a guitar detuned by 3 semitones but to keep things simpler for you I've written it in standard tuning. Sabbath devotees can tune down 3 semitones and then move all the chords up 3 frets for the full effect.

Riff 1

This main riff is played with a lot of distortion and a very fat sound (roll the treble off a bit on your amp and use a Gibson SG if you have one!). The detuning and using fatter strings will also help fatten the sound up.

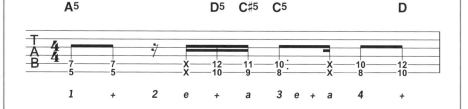

165

Beginner

Intermediate

Intermediate +

TAB

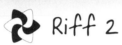 Riff 2

This is a pretty simple power chord riff, but it's big and strong! The thing to focus on here is making sure the chords ring out clearly and that your chord transitions are smooth and positive.

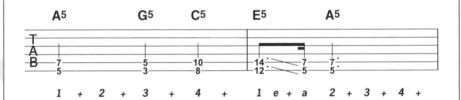

Things get a little crazy for the interlude and the solo. I've written the chords out so you can follow along but to get all the rhythm patterns for that section you will have to do some listening—it gets pretty random at points and it's supposed to be pretty free, so you should feel free to explore it, jam along and have some fun with it.

TAB STAGE

 ## Introduction

In the last section of this book we have a full TAB section. Here I've picked five awesome songs for you to work on in much greater detail.

With all these songs you should practise them slowly and carefully, making sure you are playing correctly before speeding them up. Practising slowly is the key to playing quickly!

I hope you enjoy these classics as much as I do.

justinguitar.com

TAB Guide

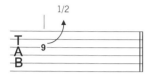

SEMI-TONE BEND: Strike the note and bend up a semi-tone (½ step).

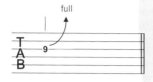

WHOLE-TONE BEND: Strike the note and bend up a whole-tone (full step).

QUARTER-TONE BEND: Strike the note and bend up a ¼ step

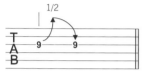

BEND & RELEASE: Strike the note and bend up as indicated, then release back to the original note.

MUFFLED STRINGS: A percussive sound is produced by laying the first hand across the string(s) without depressing, and striking them with the pick hand.

PALM MUTING: The note is partially muted by the pick hand lightly touching the string(s) just before the bridge.

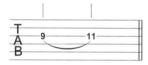

HAMMER-ON: Strike the first note with one finger, then sound the second note (on the same string) with another finger by fretting it without picking.

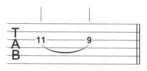

FLICK-OFF: Place both fingers on the note to be sounded, strike the first note and without picking, flick the finger off to sound the second note.

LEGATO SLIDE (GLISS): Strike the first note and then slide the same fret-hand finger up or down to the second note. The second note is not struck.

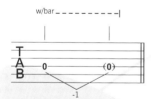

VIBRATO DIVE BAR AND RETURN: The pitch of the note or chord is dropped a specific number of steps (in rhythm) then returned to the original pitch.

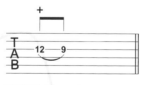

TAPPING: Hammer ('tap') the fret indicated with the pick-hand index or middle finger and flick-off to the note fretted by the fret hand.

ARPEGGIATE: Play the notes of the chord indicated by quickly rolling them from bottom to top.

RAKE: Drag the pick across the strings with a single motion.

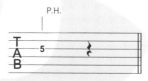

PINCH HARMONIC: The note is fretted normally and a harmonic is produced by adding the edge of the thumb or the tip of the index finger of the pick hand to the normal pick attack.

Beginner

Intermediate

Intermediate +

TAB

169

The Boys Are Back In Town

Words & Music by Phil Lynott

Beginner

Intermediate

Intermediate +

TAB

Intro   ‖: **A5** | **A5** | **B5** | **D5** :‖ *(Play x4)*

Verse 1
A5   C#m7
Guess who just got back today,
D   F#7sus4
   Them wild-eyed boys that had been away.
C#m7   F#7sus4
   Haven't changed,   hadn't much to say,
Bm7   Bm7/E
   But man, I still think them cats are crazy.
A5   C#m
   They were askin' if you were around,
D   F
   How you was, where you could be found.
C#m7   F#7sus4
   Told them you were livin' downtown,
Bm7   Bm7/E
   Driving all the old men   crazy.

Chorus 1
        A5   A5   B5   D5
The boys are back in town, (the boys are back in town,)
        A5   A5   B5   D5
I said the boys are back in town, (the boys are back in town,)
        A5   A5
The boys are back in town, (the boys are back in town,)
        B5   D5
The boys are back in town, (the boys are back in town.)

Instr. 1   ‖: **(A5)** | **(B7sus4)** | **(A/C#)** | **(D/E)** :‖

Verse 2
You know that chick that used to dance a lot?
Every night she'd be on the floor shakin' what she got.
Man, when I tell you she was cool, she was red hot,
I mean... she was steamin'!
And that time over at Johnny's place,
Well, this chick got up and she slapped Johnny's face.
Man, we just fell about the place,
If that chick don't wanna know, forget her.

Chorus 2   As Chorus 1

Instr. 2   ‖: **(A5)** | **(B7sus4)** | **(A/C#)** | **(Bm7/E)** :‖

Bridge   ‖: **Dsus4** | **D** | **C#m7** | **F#7sus4** |
                                 Spread the word around

              | **Bm7** | **Bm7/E** | **F#7sus4** | **F#7sus4** :‖
The boys are back in town

© COPYRIGHT 1976 PIPPIN THE FRIENDLY RANGER MUSIC COMPANY LIMITED.
UNIVERSAL MUSIC PUBLISHING LIMITED.
ALL RIGHTS RESERVED. INTERNATIONAL COPYRIGHT SECURED.

Verse 3	Friday night they'll be dressed to kill,
	Down at Dino's bar and grill.
	The drink will flow and blood will spill
	And if the boys wanna fight you better let 'em.
	The jukebox in the corner blasting out my favourite song,
	The nights are getting warmer and it won't be long,
	Won't be long till summer comes
	Now that the boys are here again.

Chorus 3 As Chorus 1 *(Play x2)*

Instr. 3

‖: (A5) | (A5) | (G) | (F♯m) |
| (G) | (F♯m) | (D) | (Bm7/E) :‖

‖: (A5) | (B7sus4) | (A/C♯) | (Bm7/E) :‖ *Repeat to fade*

Introduction

Here's a classic rock track from Thin Lizzy, released on the album *Jailbreak*. As well as being a great song I have amazing memories of jamming the harmony guitar solo in a band as a teenager, and I'd love for some of you to share that experience. When you and your buddy learn the parts and nail it together for the first time it's such an amazing vibe—try it and see! Note that if you are playing along with the original recording, you'll need to tune your guitar down a semitone (use your tuner: E♭, A♭, D♭, G♭, B♭, E♭).

Rhythm Parts

The rhythm guitar parts feature plenty of subtle interplay between the two guitar players: Scott Gorham and Brian Robertson. The subtly different sounds and styles that you'll hear on these two very similar guitar parts make it a very worthwhile song to study. Notes-wise, it's mainly the slight accents to the licks and riffs that create depth and contrast. You'll notice that the guitar part that is panned to the right speaker is generally slightly 'busier'.

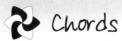 ## Chords

Although most of the tune uses pretty standard chords there are a few very interesting chords that really make the song sound 'right'. The F#7sus4 is one such chord—in some books it's written as just a regular F# but you'll hear the difference as soon as you play it. The same is the case with the Bmin7/E in the verses—it just sounds right when you play it. The Dsus4 barre chord (in the Guitar 2 part) at the start of the Bridge is another chord that some of you may not be familiar with, but it's very common in rock songs from this era.

Bm7/E

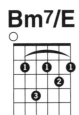

F#7sus4

Beginner

Intermediate

Intermediate +

TAB

✿ Twin Solos

The harmony guitar solos are a trademark of this track and are great fun to play. I'd recommend learning one part really well before having a crack at the other part. Jamming along with the original recording (which is tuned down a semitone) is the best strategy, and will really help you to get the sense of playing in harmony.

Note that at the end of the song there are many 'layers' of guitar—it's not just two guitars playing in harmony, as there are several other parts which would have been overdubbed in the studio. Even without overdubbing, you can still have a great time moving up the harmony parts if you are playing it with your jam buddy or in a band. When I played the song live in cover bands we used to leapfrog over each others part: guitar 1 will jump to guitar 3, then guitar 2 will jump to guitar 4, then guitar 3 will jump to guitar 5, etc, gradually getting higher up the neck. This makes it a lot of fun and a challenge to relish!

The Boys Are Back In Town

Words & Music by Phil Lynott

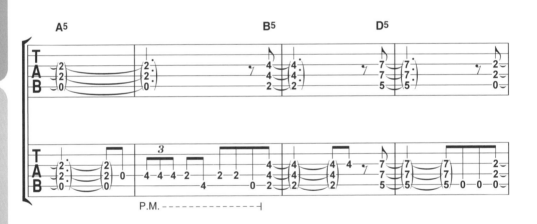

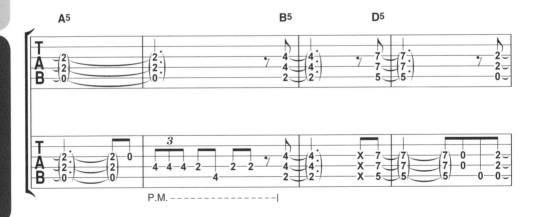

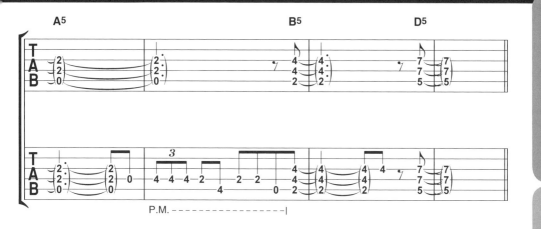

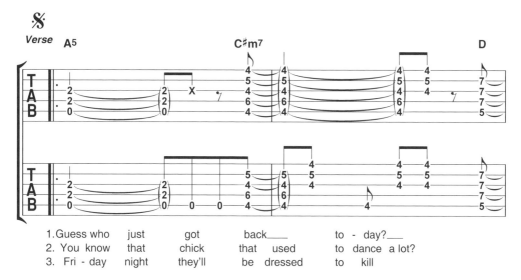

1. Guess who just got back___ to - day?___
2. You know that chick that used to dance a lot?
3. Fri - day night they'll be dressed to kill

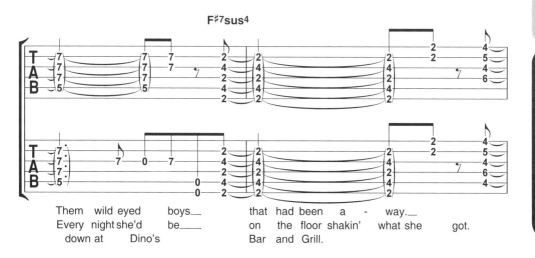

Them wild eyed boys___ that had been a - way.___
Every night she'd be___ on the floor shakin' what she got.
down at Dino's Bar and Grill.

Beginner

Intermediate

Intermediate +

TAB

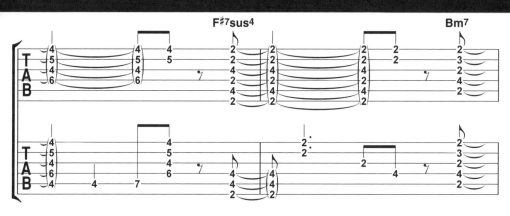

Have-n't changed, had - n't much to say,
Man, when I tell you she was cool, she was red hot!
The drink will flow and blood will spill, and if the

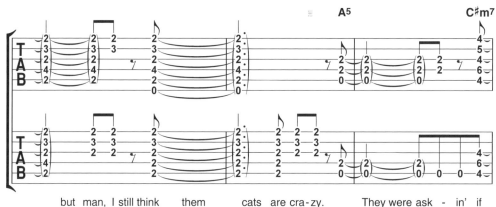

but man, I still think them cats are cra-zy.
I mean she was steamin'!
boys wan-na fight you better let 'em.

They were ask - in' if
And that time over at
The juke - box in the

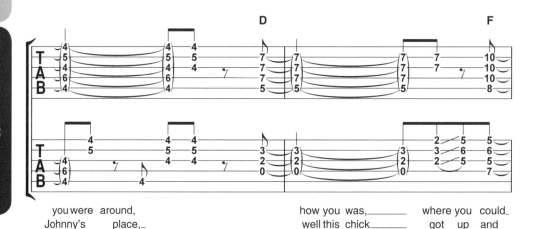

you were around,
Johnny's place,_
corner blastin' out my favourite song

how you was,_____ where you could_
well this chick_____ got up and
The nights are getting warm and it

176

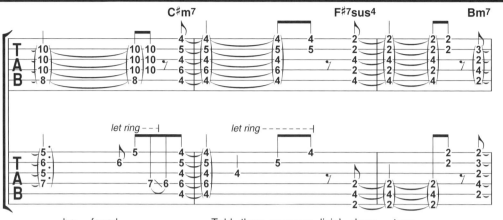

__ be found.
she slapped Johnny's face.
won't be long

Told them you were livin' down - town,
Man, we just fell about the place.
won't be long 'til sum-mer comes,

Chorus

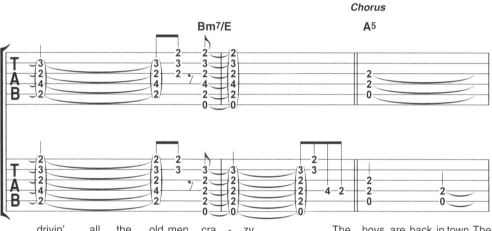

drivin' all the old men cra - zy.__
If that chick don't wanna know, forget her.
now that the boys are here__ again.

The boys are back in town. The

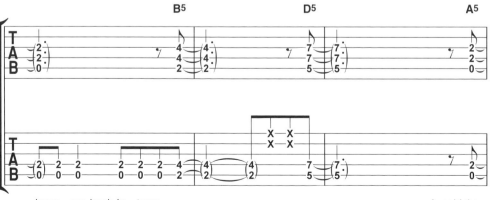

boys are back in town.

I said the

Beginner

Intermediate

Intermediate +

TAB

177

Beginner

Intermediate

Intermediate +

TAB

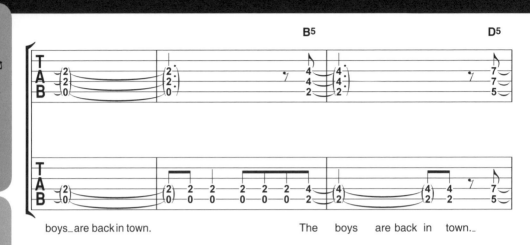

boys_are back in town. The boys are back in town._

To Coda

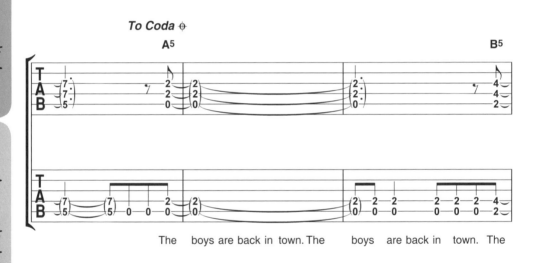

The boys are back in town. The boys are back in town. The

Instr.

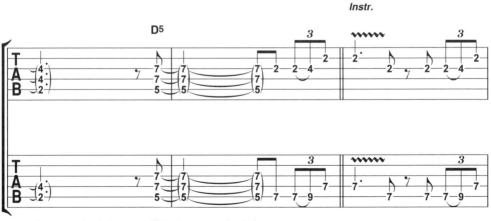

boys are back in town. The boys are back in town.

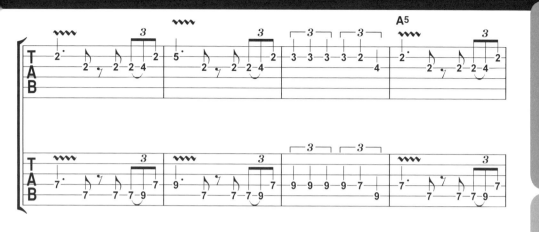

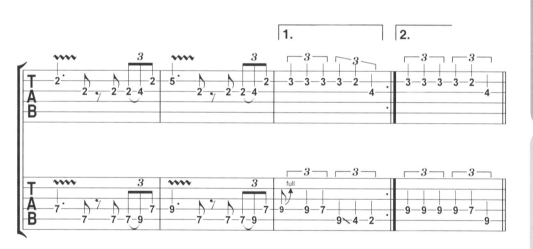

Bridge

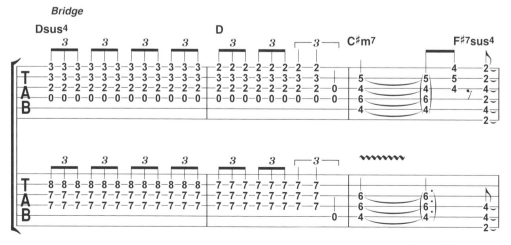

Spread the word

179

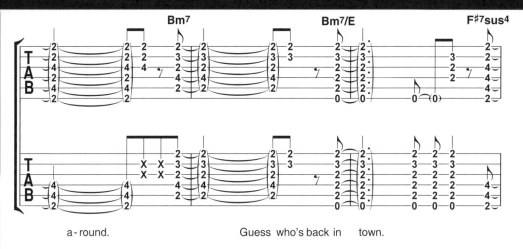

a - round.   Guess who's back in   town.

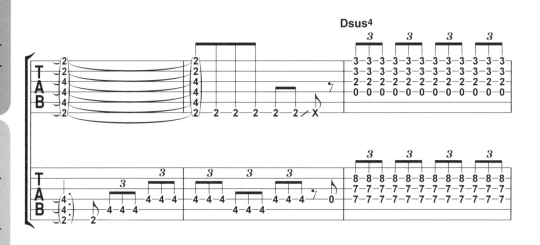

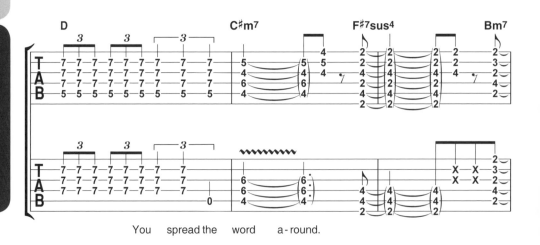

You   spread the   word   a - round.

Bm7/E

F♯7sus4

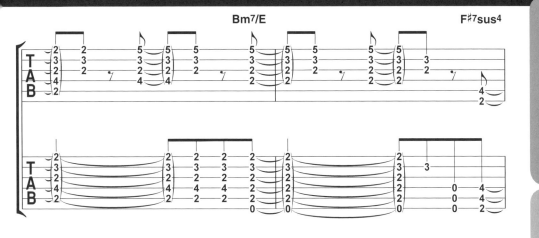

D.S. al Coda

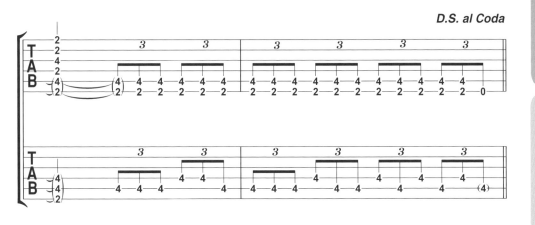

Coda

A5

B5

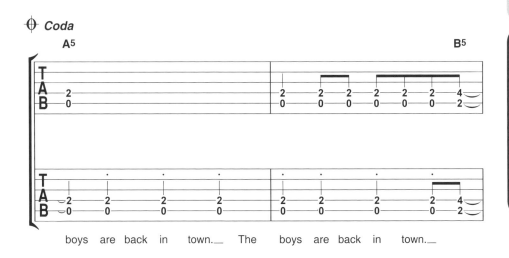

boys   are   back   in   town.__   The   boys   are   back   in   town.__

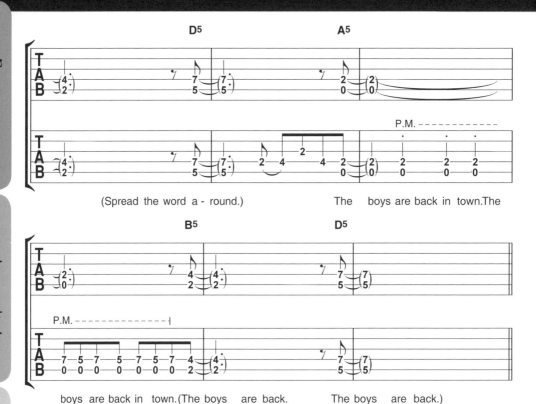

(Spread the word a - round.)   The   boys are back in town.The

boys are back in town.(The boys   are back.   The boys   are back.)

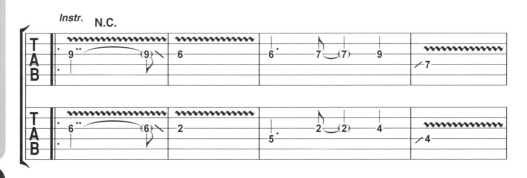

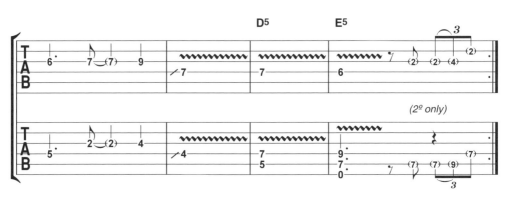

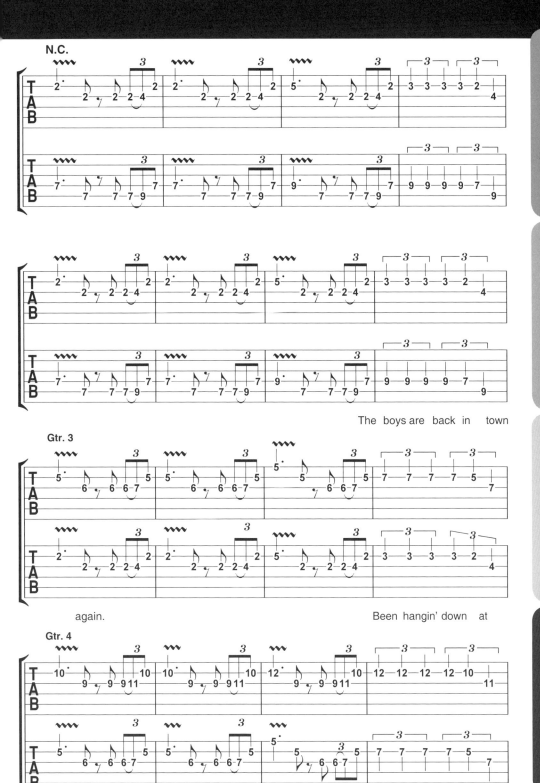

The boys are back in town

again.   Been hangin' down at

Dino's.   The boys are back in town

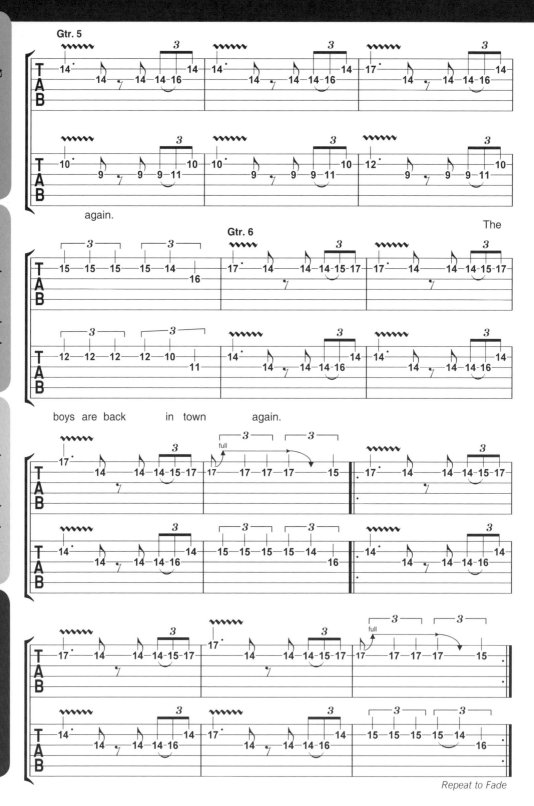

Repeat to Fade

Sultans Of Swing
Words & Music by Mark Knopfler

Introduction

This Dire Straits hit from 1979 is a bone fide classic guitar song if there ever was one. Mark Knopfler plays with taste, raw energy and elegance, all of which will make learning this song extremely rewarding!

I recommend learning this song in stages, starting with the rhythm guitar. This will help you understand the underlying harmony of the song, and as a result the licks and solos will make more sense.

Rhythm

The rhythm on the recording uses a slightly tricky technique, but can be simplified to this pattern, which I suggest you learn first. The X represents a percussive hit, where you will mute the strings with the edge of your strumming hand whilst continuing to strum the strings.

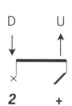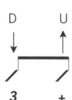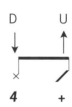

Once you've nailed this technique, you can add in some fast sixteenth-note strums before the first percussive hit. This will most likely take some slow and careful practice. We're switching briefly from eighth-note to sixteenth-note strumming, so the + after 1 will be played as a down-strum (it was previously an up-strum). This goes against the grain a little, but will flow nicely once you've mastered it.

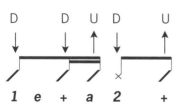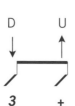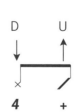

185

Sultans Of Swing

Words & Music by Mark Knopfler

Beginner

Intermediate

Intermediate +

TAB

Intro ‖: Dm | Dm | Dm | Dm :‖

Verse 1

        Dm
You get a shiver in the dark
  |C   B♭ |A   A
It's raining in the park but meantime
Dm |C   B♭ |A   A
   South of the river you stop and you hold every - thing
F   F   C   C
   A band is blowing Dixie double four time
B♭   B♭   (Dm)
   You feel alright   when you hear that music ring

Link 1 | Dm | Dm B♭ | C | C |

Verse 2

You step inside but you don't see too many faces
Coming in out of the rain to hear the jazz go down
Too much competition in other places
But the horns they're blowing that sound

Chorus

Dm | Dm B♭ | C |C   B♭ |
             Way on downsouth
C   C   ‖:Dm | Dm C B♭|C | C :‖
  Way on downsouth London town

Verse 3

You check out Guitar George he knows all the chords
Mind he's strictly rhythm he doesn't want to make it cry or sing
And an old guitar is all he can afford
When he gets up under the lights to play his thing

Link 2 | Dm | Dm B♭ | C | C |

Verse 4

And Harry doesn't mind if he doesn't make the scene
He's got a day-time job, he's doing alright
He can play the honky-tonk just like anything
Saving it up for Friday night,

Chorus 2 With the Sultans, with the Sultans of Swing.

Verse 5

And a crowd of young boys they're fooling around in the corner
Drunk and dressed in their best brown baggies and their platform soles
They don't give a damn about any trumpet playing band
It ain't what they call rock and roll

Chorus 3 And the Sultans, the Sultans played Creole.

Gtr. Solo Verse & Chorus Sequence

© COPYRIGHT 1978 STRAITJACKET SONGS LIMITED.
UNIVERSAL MUSIC PUBLISHING LIMITED.
ALL RIGHTS RESERVED. INTERNATIONAL COPYRIGHT SECURED.

Verse 6 And then the man he steps right up to the microphone
And says at last just as the time bell rings
'Thank you goodnight, now it's time to go home'
And he makes fast with one more thing

Chorus 4 'We are the Sultans, we are the Sultans of Swing.'

Guitar solo 2 ‖: Dm C │ B♭   │ C   │ C   :‖ *Play to fade*

Licks

This song is an amazing lick-fest and if you are looking for new, impressive licks to add to your vocabulary, this is a great song to steal some ideas from. There are far too many for me to go into detail about each one, so I'm going to pick out some of my favourites, as well as the licks that need a little 'trick' to master them, and therefore require a little more explanation. These licks are labelled in the TAB, and explained in the following lesson.

Do remember that Mark Knopfler doesn't use a pick—instead, he plays with fingers p (thumb), i (index) and m (middle) only, so plectrum players may find some of these passages very difficult until they develop the right technique!

Lick 1

This is a super classy lick that requires great bending control. While holding the bend at the 8th fret, you need to reach out with your little finger to play the 9th fret on the thinnest string. Then release the bend, play the 7th fret and get back with some accurate bouncing bends on the third string.

Beginner

Intermediate

Intermediate +

TAB

 ### Lick 2

There are a lot of arpeggios in Mark Knopfler's playing, and this one is based on an A triad. I'd recommend trying to work out the 'function' of each note in the solo against the chord. It requires good knowledge of theory and chord; its proper name is slightly scary—'Harmonic Analysis'—but it's this skill that will enable you to understand these licks properly and then be able to use them in your improvisations. Bars 3,4 and 5 of the first solo outline the chords perfectly—see if you can find other 'obvious' arpeggio-based licks!

 ### Lick 3

This is another country-influenced lick that requires great bending technique and a sneaky little finger barre. Can you see how it is outlining the notes of the F chord, which is played by the rhythm guitar? Getting used to visually analysing licks and the chords that they are played over can give you a practical sense of 'Harmonic Analysis' without getting too bogged down in theory!

 ### Lick 4

This lick is classy, simple and elegant! It's just a pentatonic scale but the note choices and the little half muted note on the thinnest string give it a more complex character. This is a 'must steal'!

Beginner

Intermediate

Intermediate +

TAB

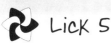 Lick 5

Because Knopfler plays with his fingers and not a pick, this lick will feel awkward until you get the technique in the picking hand right. The middle part can be done a few ways (and I'm not positive I know which fingers Knopfler uses) but the first three notes should certainly be played p (thumb), i (index finger), m (middle finger) and the last four notes in bar 1 will be played p, (hammer), i, m and then I would pick the last note of the lick. Take it slowly and see if you can 'feel' the right fingers to use—find out what is comfortable for you.

Lick 6

Everyone loves this lick: the fast climax! The picking hand is the bit that causes the most problems but it's pretty easy once you know the trick! Start each beat with the thumb (p), then flick off, then your thumb will go over and play string 2, and lastly finger 1 will play the thinnest string. Practise it slowly, over and over—just the first bar—you will see that it's just a 4-note sequence that repeats. Once you get that comfortable, try going into the second bar, which is only one note different! The only hard part is working through the end of the 2nd and 4th bars where the pattern hiccups and leaves out the flick-off. It's a great lick and a very satisfying one to master!

Sultans Of Swing

Words & Music by Mark Knopfler

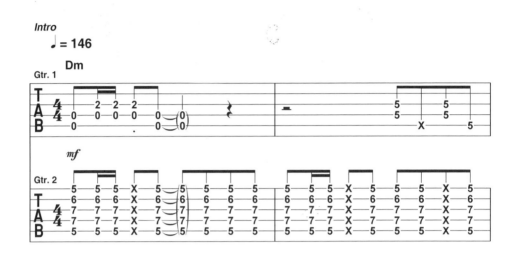

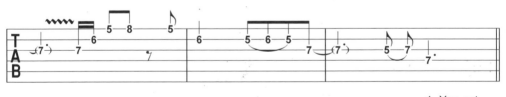

1. You get

Verse

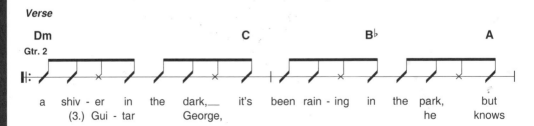

a   shiv - er   in   the   dark,___   it's   been   rain - ing   in   the   park,   but
(3.) Gui - tar   George,   he   knows

191

you feel al - right_____ when you hear that mu - sic ring.
when he gets up under the lights_____ to play his thing.

2. You step in - side but you don't see too ma -ny fa-
4. And Harry doesn't mind if he does -n't_

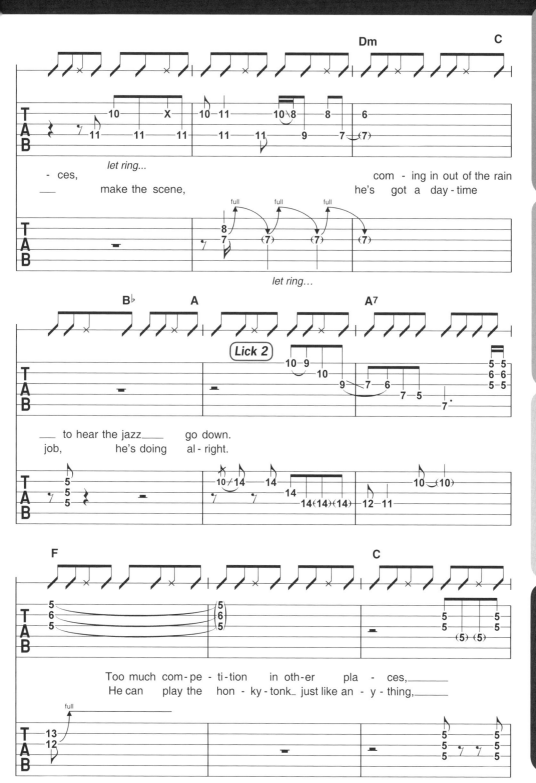

193

Sultans Of Swing (cont.)

Beginner

Intermediate

Intermediate +

TAB

but the horns   they're blow-ing that
sav - ing it   up   for   Fri - day   night

Chorus

sound,___

way on
with the Sul-

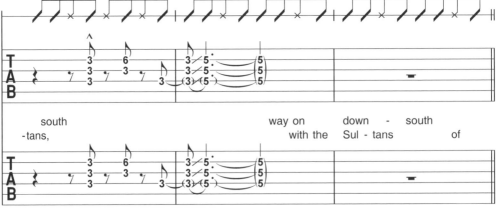

south   way on   down - south
-tans,   with the   Sul - tans   of

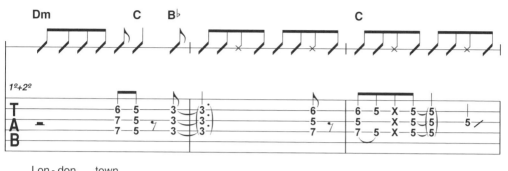

Lon - don   town.
swing.

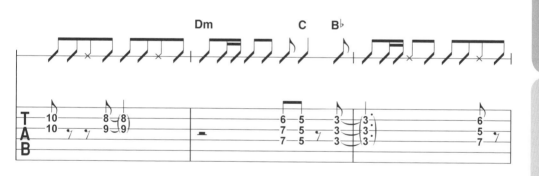

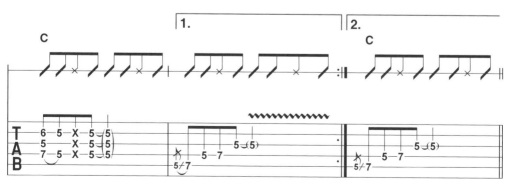

3. You check out   5. And a

Beginner

Intermediate

Intermediate +

TAB

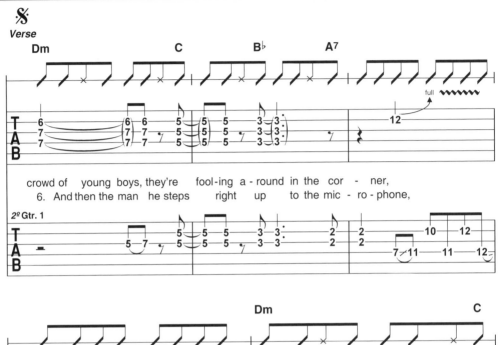

crowd of young boys, they're fool-ing a - round in the cor - ner,
6. And then the man he steps right up to the mic - ro - phone,

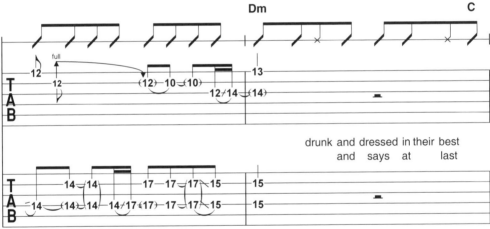

drunk and dressed in their best
and says at last

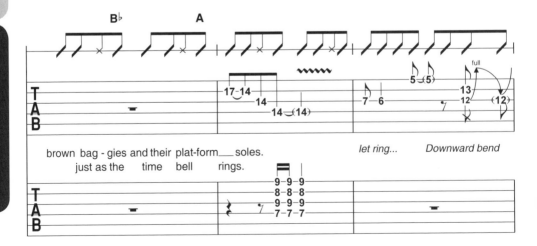

brown bag - gies and their plat-form___ soles.
just as the time bell rings.

let ring... Downward bend

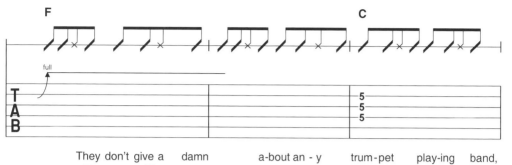

F   **C**

They don't give a   damn   a-bout an - y   trum-pet   play-ing   band,
Thank you 'Good - night,   now it's time   to   go   home'.

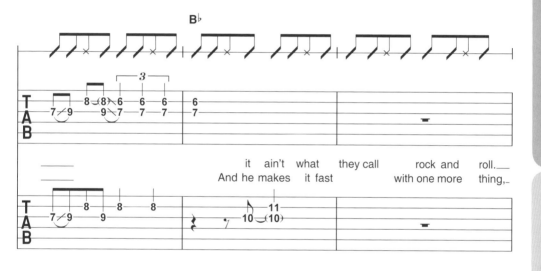

B♭

it   ain't   what   they call   rock and   roll.___
And he makes   it fast   with one more   thing,_

Chorus **Dm**   **B♭**   **C**

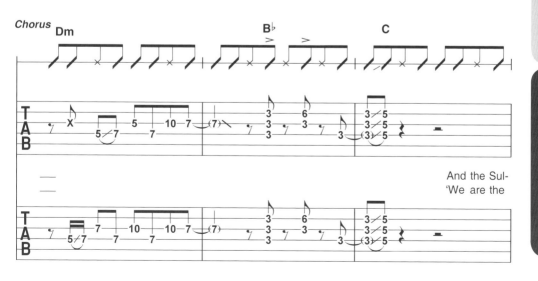

And the Sul-
'We are the

197

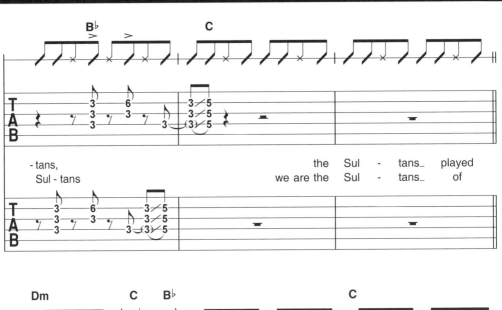

- tans,
Sul - tans

the Sul - tans_ played
we are the Sul - tans_ of

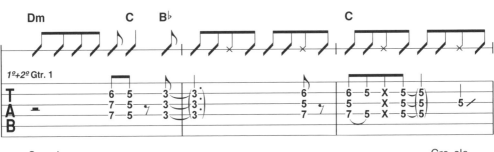

Cre - ole.
swing.'

Cre - ole

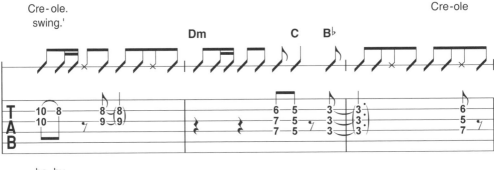

ba - by,

To Coda ⊕

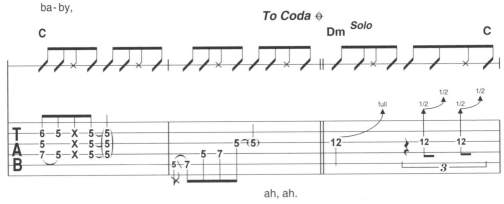

ah, ah.

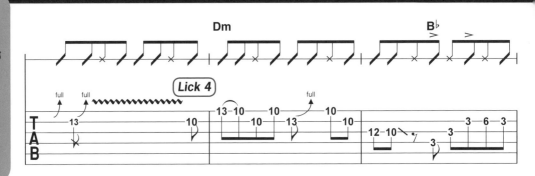

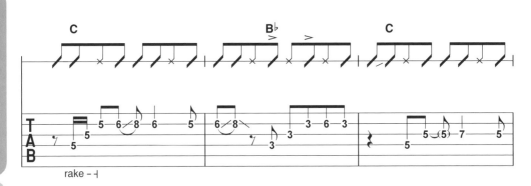

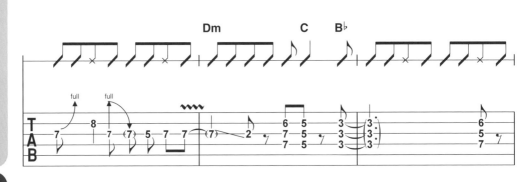

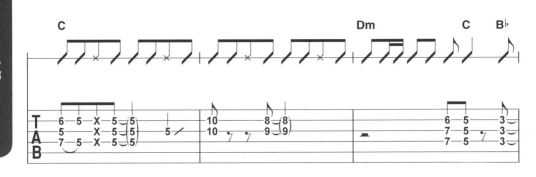

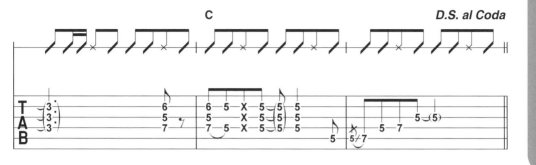

Coda

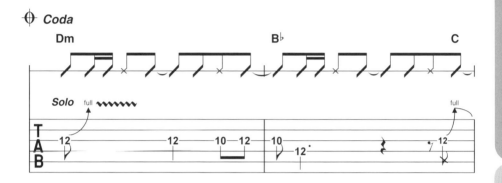

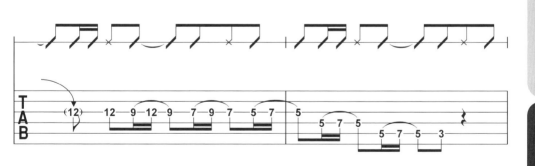

Gtr. 2 *cont. ad lib. sim.*

Beginner

Intermediate

Intermediate +

TAB

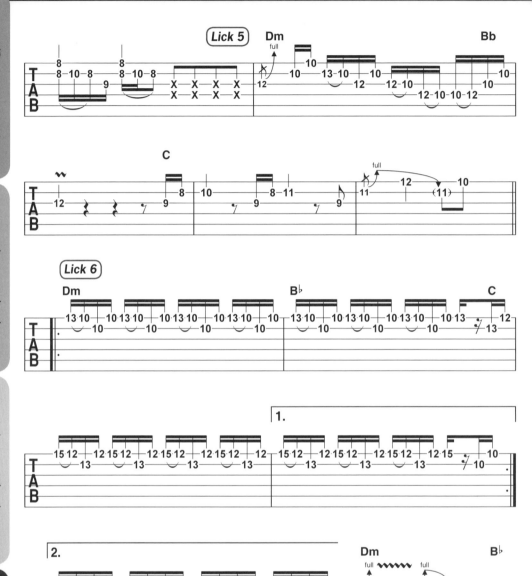

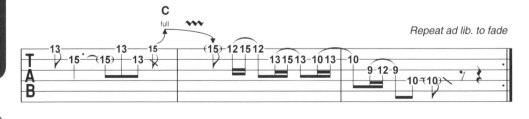

Sweet Home Alabama

Words & Music by Ronnie Van Zant, Ed King & Gary Rossington

 ## Introduction

Lynyrd Skynyrd's 'Sweet Home Alabama' is an all-time classic country rock guitar song with loads of great licks, fun riffs and many layers of guitar. Is there anybody who doesn't want to play this riff?

 ## Main Riff (Intro)

This guitar riff—one of the most famous ever written—deserves special attention, and to get it sounding just like the record will take a fair bit of practice. It's easy to do a poor imitation of the riff, but to play it correctly you'll have to slow it down and learn it bit by bit.

Start by playing through the chords—this will give you an overall feel for this section. There's nothing too difficult here really, and the fingering for the riff should be pretty obvious—the lick at the end of bar 2 is all played with finger 2 until the second last note, for which you'll use finger 3. The fingering for the ascending lick (Guitar 1, bar 4) isn't set in stone—use whichever fingers you feel comfortable with.

What makes a bigger difference than you might imagine is the picking, so much so that I have written it in for you. It follows the common 'alternate picking' patterns of down on the beat and '+'s and up on the two sixteenth-notes in between. The exception is the last ascending lick where it breaks that pattern, as far as I can tell.

Your best strategy will be to play along with the original recording at half speed (using slowing-down software). It will really help you find the right feel as well as making sure that your timing is accurate—just make sure you learn it correctly and play it very slowly before trying to play along at speed, or you will be forced to rush into mistakes!

Sweet Home Alabama

Words & Music by Ronnie Van Zant, Ed King & Gary Rossington

Beginner

Intermediate

Intermediate +

TAB

Intro   ‖: D   Cadd⁹ |G   G   :‖

Verse 1
|D   C |G
   Big wheels keep on turning
|D   C |G
   Carry me home to see my kin
|D   C |G
   Singing songs about the Southland
|D   C |G
   I miss Alabama once again (*And I think its a sin, yes.*)

Interlude   ‖: D   C |G   :‖

Verse 2
Well I heard mister Young sing about her,
Well, I heard old Neil put her down
Well, I hope Neil Young will remember
A Southern man don't need him around anyhow.

Chorus 1
|D   C |G   C |
   Sweet home Alabama
|D   C |G
   Where the skies are so blue,
|D   C |G   C |
   Sweet Home Alabama
|D   C |G   F   C |
   Lord, I'm coming home to you.

Solo 1   ‖: D   Cadd⁹ |G   :‖

Verse 3
|D   C |G   F   C |(D)
    In Birming - ham they love the Governor, (boo, hoo, hoo)
Now we all did what we could do
Now Watergate does not bother me
Does your conscience bother you? Tell the truth.

Chorus 2
As Chorus 1
|D   C |G
...Lord I'm coming home to you.

Solo 2   ‖: D   C |G   :‖ (*Play x10*)

Verse 4
Now Muscle Shoals has got the Swampers
And they've been known to pick a song or two (*yes they do*),
Lord they get me off so much
They pick me up when I'm feeling blue
Now how 'bout you?

© COPYRIGHT 1974 EMI LONGITUDE MUSIC/UNIVERSAL MUSIC CORPORATION/
FULL KEEL MUSIC CO./SONGS OF UNIVERSAL INC.
UNIVERSAL/MCA MUSIC LIMITED.
ALL RIGHTS RESERVED. INTERNATIONAL COPYRIGHT SECURED.

Chorus 3	As Chorus 1
Chorus 4	As Chorus 2
Outro	‖: D C |G G :‖ *Repeat to fade*

 # Figure 1

There are at least three guitar parts playing for most of the track, but the other obvious rhythm part is shown in the TAB as 'Figure 1' in the lower (Guitar 2) part. It's a very simple line which weaves together with the main riff brilliantly. It's a great example of simple but effective playing. The part isn't difficult in itself, but you must work on getting the rhythm right because if you don't, the two guitar parts won't weave together, and the whole thing may fall apart! That said, the figure isn't strictly followed when it's repeated in the verses, although it's pretty close, nonetheless.

 # Interlude

This is another awesome riff and again the fretting hand has it pretty easy—the important detail is getting the rhythm and picking right, so I have written the picking in, and you should have a listen to the original at a nice, slow tempo (using software) and play along! The fretting hand does have some tricky slides which will probably take some work before they sound smooth, but with practice the part will flow together perfectly.

Beginner

Intermediate

Intermediate +

TAB

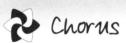 Chorus

The chorus has a fantastic rhythm guitar part—it's a blues-based '6th' chord riff, which includes some really satisfying fills. You'll need a decent stretch in your fretting hand to be able to play this section comfortably. The trickiest bit is between the 4th and 5th bars, where you play a little slide and then come back onto the chord on the 'and' after beat 1 in the next bar—it's not hard really, just a bit unexpected and so might require extra attention!

 Solos

The second guitar solo has some amazing licks to steal, and some very tricky bits to master!

The monster fast lick that starts after 4 bars of the solo (*) is rhythmically very complicated—you'll have difficulty replicating the solo exactly, and I'd wager that it's never been played the same way twice! I'd recommend learning the licks and doing the best you can rather than trying to precisely replicate the recording, unless you are a big fan and prepared to put in many hours of practice.

The 8th bar of the solo (**), where the manic part turns into even sixteenth notes, is a great lick to steal. It's based around the G Major Pentatonic shape, and you'll find plenty of other licks following it. Make sure you can relate the notes in the solo back to their parent scale, which in this case is the G Major Pentatonic. Doing so will help you make sense of the note choices and allow you to use the licks in your own improvisations.

Also worth exploring is the excellent use of slides within many of the licks, which is a trademark of this Southern rock style and a very creative concept, worth exploring.

Sweet Home Alabama

Words & Music by Ronnie Van Zant, Ed King & Gary Rossington

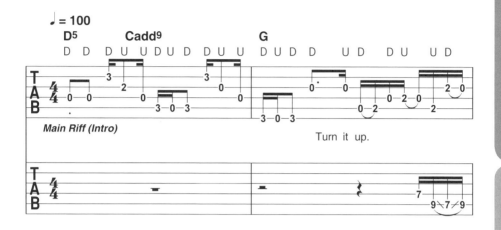

Main Riff (Intro)

Turn it up.

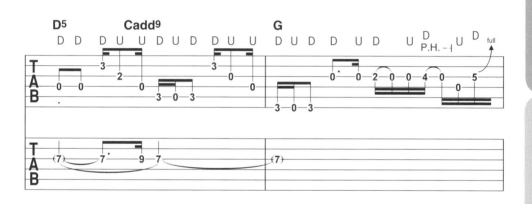

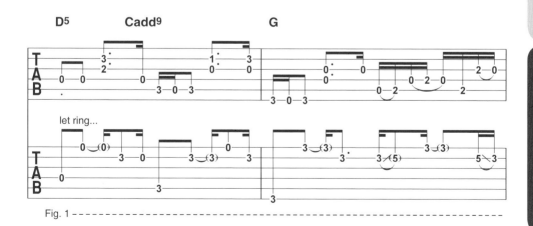

Fig. 1

Sweet Home Alabama (cont.)

Beginner

Intermediate

Intermediate +

TAB

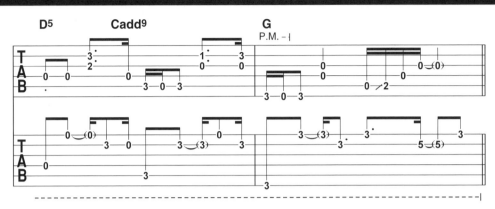

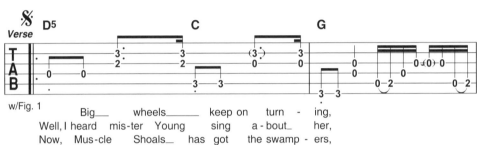

w/Fig. 1

Big___ wheels_____ keep on turn - ing,
Well, I heard mis-ter Young sing a - bout_ her,
Now, Mus-cle Shoals_ has got the swamp - ers,

car - ry me home to see my kin.
well, I heard old Ne - il put her down.
and they've been known to pick a song or two.___

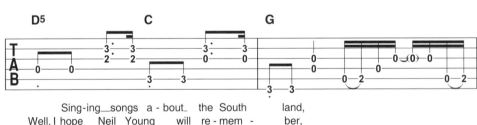

Sing-ing___songs a - bout_ the South land,
Well, I hope Neil Young will re - mem - ber,
Lord, they get me off___ so much.

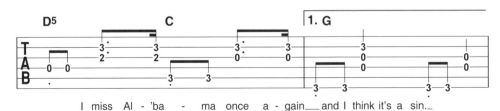

I miss Al - 'ba - ma once a - gain___ and I think it's a sin._
a South-ern man don't need him a -
they pick me up___when I'm feel - ing blue,

208

Interlude

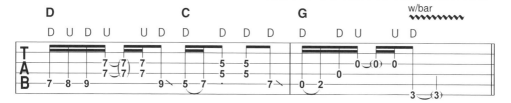

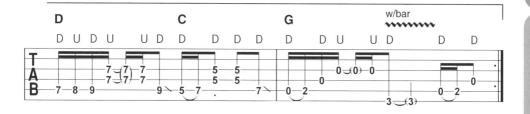

2.3.

G

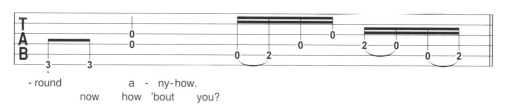

- round   a - ny-how.
        now   how 'bout   you?

Chorus

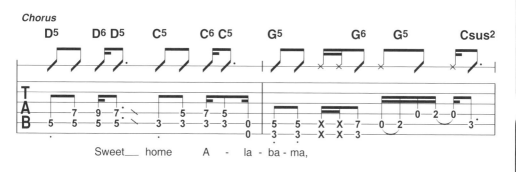

Sweet__ home   A - la - ba - ma,

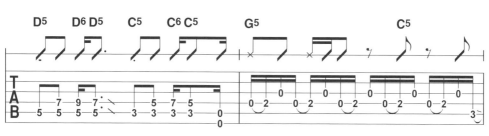

where   the skies   are   so blue.__

209

Beginner

Intermediate

Intermediate +

TAB

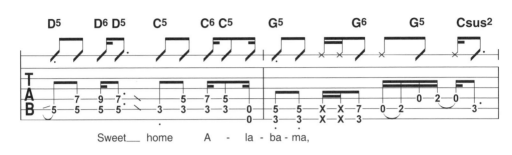

Sweet__ home A - la - ba - ma,

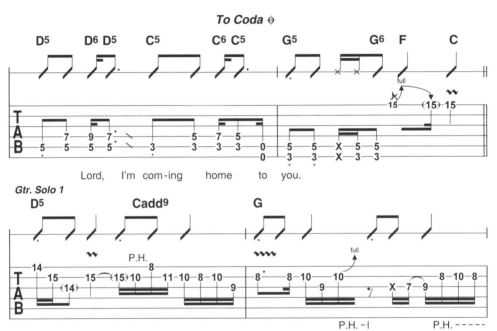

Lord,   I'm com-ing   home   to   you.

Gtr. Solo 1

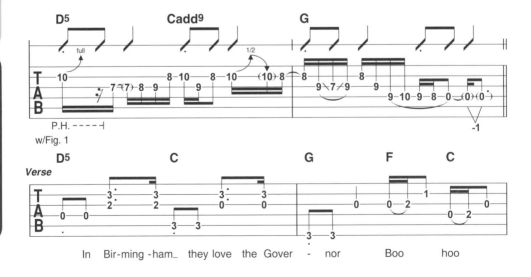

In Bir-ming -ham_ they love the Gover - nor   Boo   hoo

210

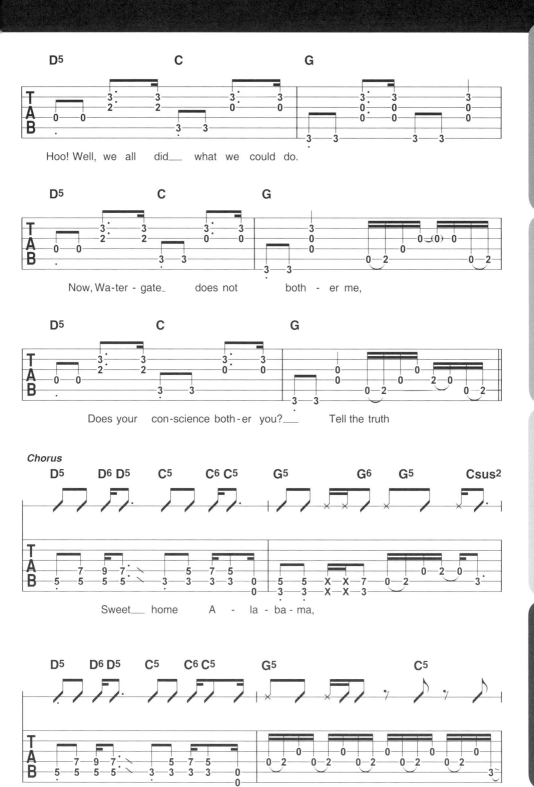

Hoo! Well, we all did__ what we could do.

Now, Wa-ter - gate_ does not both - er me,

Does your con-science both-er you?__ Tell the truth

Chorus

Sweet__ home A - la - ba - ma,

where the skies are so blue.__

Beginner

Intermediate

Intermediate +

TAB

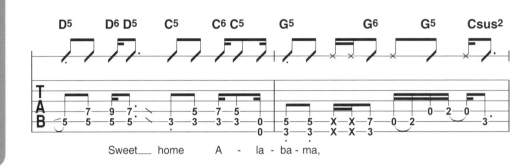

Sweet__ home   A - la - ba - ma,

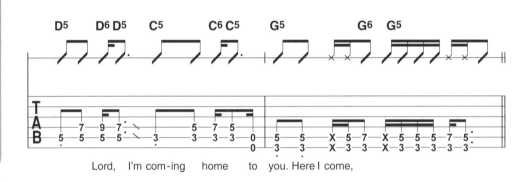

Lord,   I'm com-ing   home   to   you. Here I come,

Gtr. solo 2

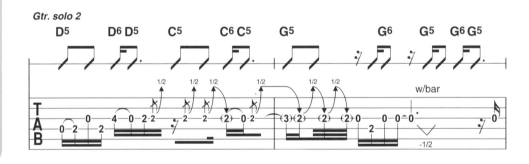

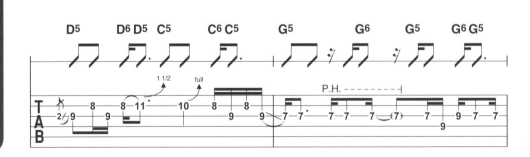

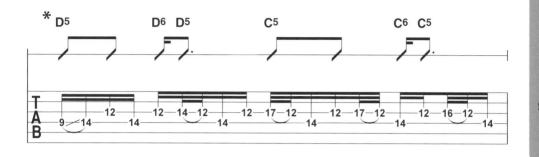

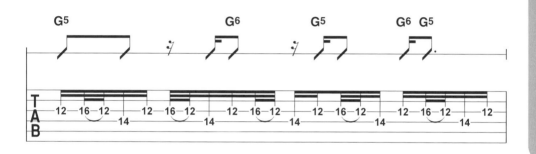

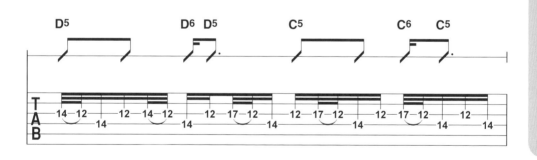

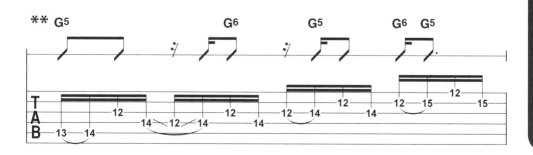

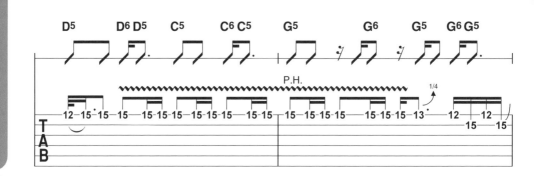

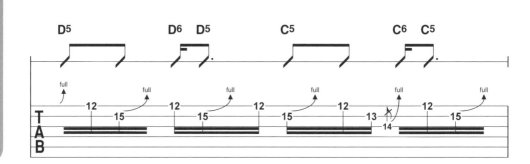

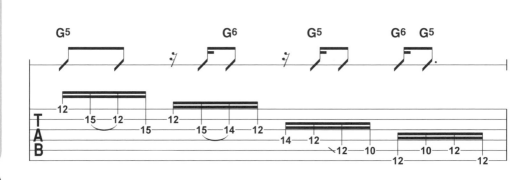

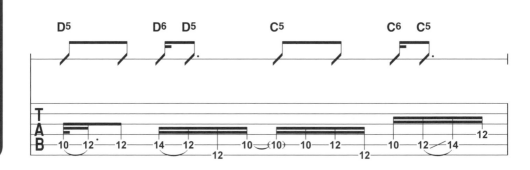

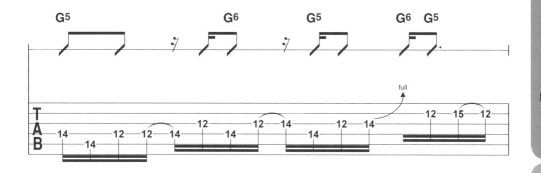

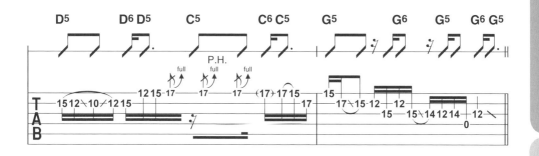

Interlude

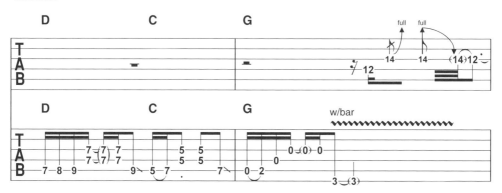

D.S. al Coda

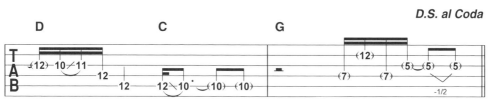

Harm.------------------|

215

Sweet Home Alabama (cont.)

Beginner

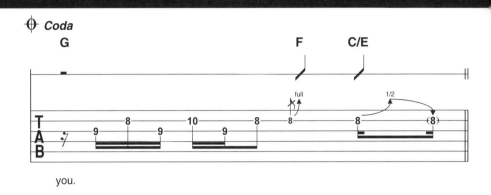

you.

Intermediate

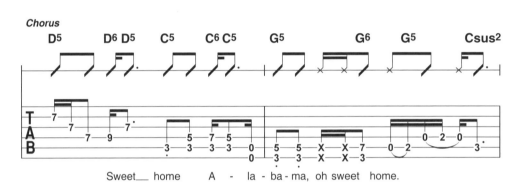

Sweet__ home   A - la - ba - ma, oh sweet home.

Intermediate +

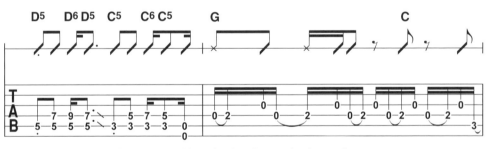

where the skies are so blue (and   the gov-'nor's true).

TAB

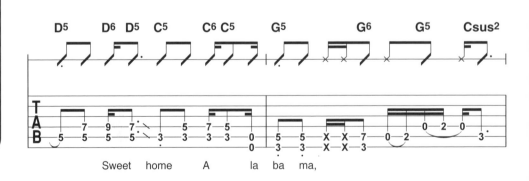

Sweet   home   A   la   ba   ma,

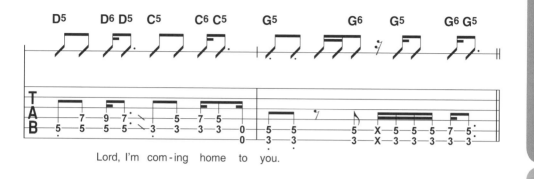

Lord, I'm com-ing home to you.

Outro

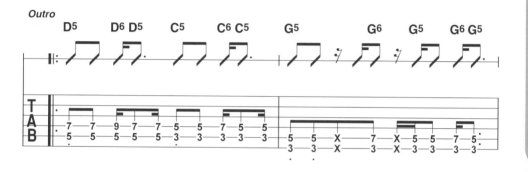

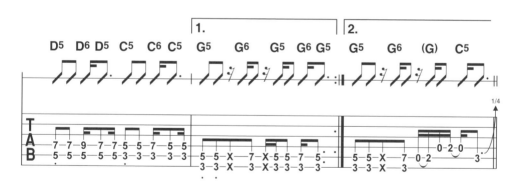

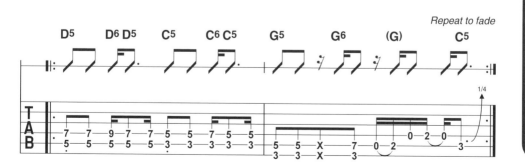

217

You Shook Me All Night Long

Words & Music by Angus Young, Malcolm Young & Brian Johnson

Beginner

Intermediate

Intermediate +

TAB

Intro   ‖: Dsus⁴ | Dsus⁴ | D⁵ | D⁵ :‖

Play **riff 1 (x2)**

riff 1 (x3)

Verse 1
She was a fast machine, she kept her motor clean,
She was the best damn woman that I've ever seen.
She had the sightless eyes, tellin' me no lies,
Knockin' me out with those American thighs.
Takin' more than her share, had me fightin' for air,
She told me to come but I was already there.

Pre-chorus 1   **(riff 1)**
'Cause the walls start shakin',
The earth was quakin',

D
My mind was achin'
|G⁵   D⁵ G⁵   D |
And we were makin'   it (And..)

Chorus 1   (D) G⁵ |Cadd⁹ G/B |D |Cadd⁹
And you shook me all   night long,
G/B |G⁵ |Cadd⁹ G/B |D |Cadd⁹ G/B |
   Yeah, you shook me all   night long.   (Workin'..)

Verse 2
Workin' double time on the seduction line,
She was one of a kind, she's just mine, all mine.
Wanted no applause, just another course,
Made a meal outta me and came back for more.
Had to cool me down to take another round,
Now I'm back in the ring to take another swing.

Pre-chorus 2 'Cause the walls were shakin',
The earth was quakin',
My mind was achin'
And we were makin' it.

Chorus 2   And you shook me all night long,
Yeah, you shook me all night long, and knocked me out, babe.

Chorus 3   You shook me all night long,
You had me shakin', baby,
G⁵ |Cadd⁹ G/B |D
You shook me all   night long,

© COPYRIGHT 1980 J. ALBERT & SON PTY. LIMITED.
ALL RIGHTS RESERVED. INTERNATIONAL COPYRIGHT SECURED.

218

(cont.)

G5   **D/A**
You shook me,

D/A
Well, you took me.

Guitar solo

Play **riff 2 (x2)**

Play chorus sequence (x2)

...You really took me in.

Chorus 4   As Chorus 1

Chorus 5

           G5 |**Csus2 G/B** |**D**
Yeah, yeah, you shook me all   night long,

|**Csus2**   **G/B** |
   You really got me in.

G5 |**Csus2 G/B** |**D** |**Csus2**
You shook me all   night long,

          G/B |**D**
Yeah, you shook me,

|**Csus2**   **G/B** |**D D**   **D**
   Yeah, you shook me   all night long!

Introduction

This classic AC/DC tune from *Back In Black* (1980) has all the trademarks of the greatest rock band of all time: big riffs, a screaming solo and an anthemic chorus!

Intro

This part is based around a kind of D-shape—you'll use finger 1 on the third string and finger 3 on the second string. You'll have to reach up to the 10th fret with finger 4, use finger 1 for the note on the 7th fret and then slide the shape down to the regular D position. Notice that you'll have to play the note on the 4th fret with your little finger because you should try and hold the chord down.

Beginner

Intermediate

Intermediate +

TAB

 Verse

You'll often see this section played using a Cadd9 chord (like a 'big' G with fingers 1 & 2 moved down a string), which despite making the chord changes a load easier, isn't the way it was played on the record. To do it for real you need to get your G to C change happening quickly and accurately! Make sure you mute where needed with the outer palm of your picking hand and remember that the secret to playing AC/DC songs really well is the rhythm! You must get the groove locked in a tight. As usual, playing along with the original recording is the best strategy.

Chorus

The chorus stays with simple open chords—you'll have finger 3 as an anchor now, so the changes should be pretty easy. There is a 'climb up' to deal with so you will need to make sure you are picking accurately and hitting the right notes—it's a pretty consistent pattern. The Guitar 2 part is similar—it outlines the 'climb up' and includes some more arpeggiated patterns. If you are playing on your own then stick with Guitar 1.

Beginner

Intermediate

Intermediate +

TAB

 Solo

The solo in this song is classic Angus Young, full of bluesy licks played with attitude on a Gibson SG through a Marshall amp—it certainly ain't noise pollution! It starts with Pattern 1 Pentatonic, (lesson IM-153 on the website) so fingering here should be obvious, and then on the climb up, starting at the end of the 5th bar (marked *), you'll use finger 2 for the slide—this will leave you in the right place to be using finger 3 for the bends a couple of bars later.

Then we jump up to Pattern 1 Pentatonic, up the octave (marked **), and there are some very tasty licks here worth stealing. My personal favourite starts at the end of the 4th last bar with the little semitone bend on the 17th fret (marked ***). It's a sublime lick.

You would do well to break this solo down and practise each individual lick, as there are so many that are useful and sound awesome mixed in with your blues vocabulary. It's largely based on the G Dorian mode, but a great exercise for you would be to work out the function of each note over the chord playing underneath—you will find a strong relationship between the note choices and the chords played—this kind of understanding will help you use ideas the solos you learn to create your own solos.

You Shook Me All Night Long

Words & Music by Angus Young, Malcolm Young & Brian Johnson

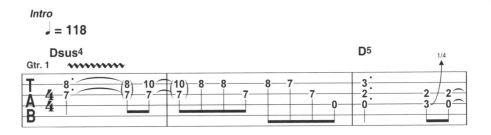

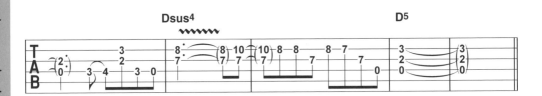

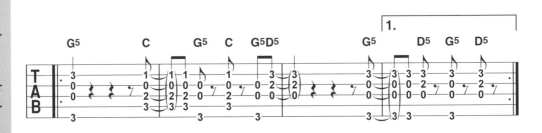

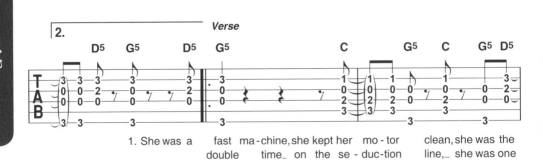

1. She was a fast ma-chine, she kept her mo-tor clean, she was the
double time_ on the se-duc-tion line,_ she was one

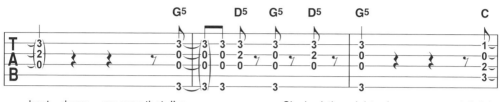

best damn wo-man that I've   ev-er seen. She had the sight - less eyes   tell-in'
of   a   kind,   she's just mine   all mine, Want ed no   ap-plause   just an-

me no   lies,_   Kock-in' me out_ with those A - me - ri - can thighs. Tak - in'
-oth-er course. Made a meal out-ta me_   and came back for   more.   Had to

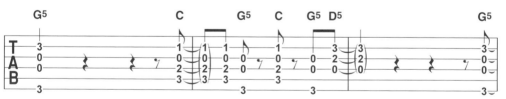

more that her   share   had me fight-in' for air._   she told me to come but I was
cool   me down to take an - oth - er round,   now I'm back the ring_ to take an

Pre-chorus

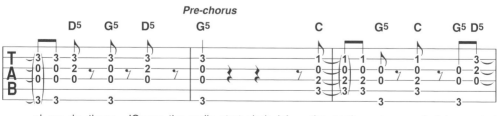

al-rea-dy there. 'Cause the walls start shak- in',   the earth was quak- in',my mind
-oth-er   swing. 'Cause the walls were shak- in',   the earth was quak- in',my mind

Beginner

Intermediate

Intermediate +

TAB

223

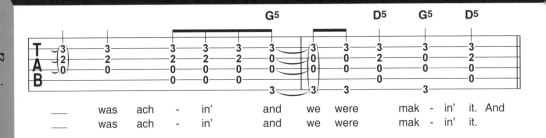

was   ach - in'   and   we   were   mak - in' it. And
was   ach - in'   and   we   were   mak - in' it.

Chorus

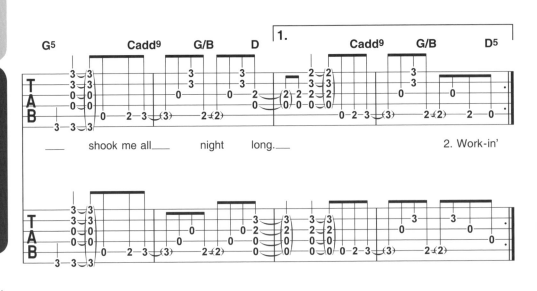

you   shook me all___   night   long.___   Yeah, you

___   shook me all___   night   long.___   2. Work-in'

2.

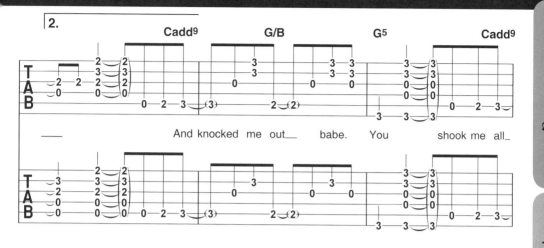

And knocked me out__ babe. You shook me all_

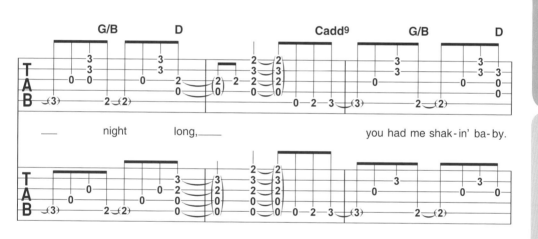

___ night long,___ you had me shak-in' ba-by.

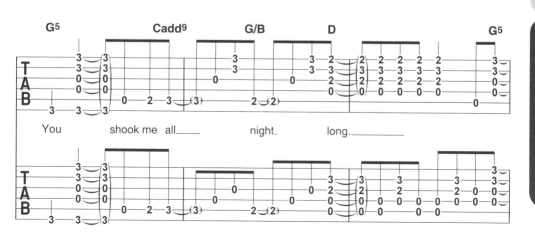

You shook me all____ night_ long._____

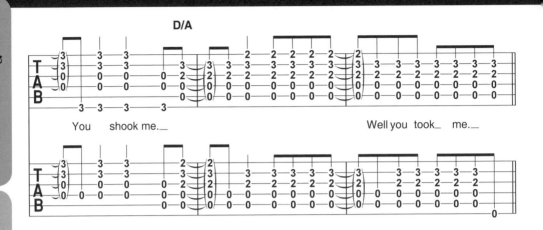

You   shook me.___   Well you took___ me.___

Solo

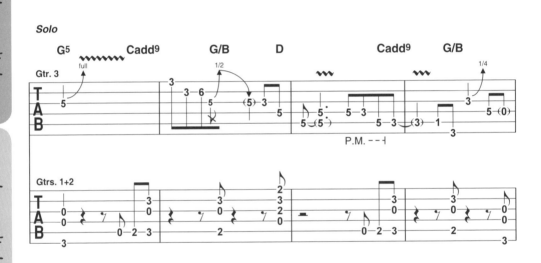

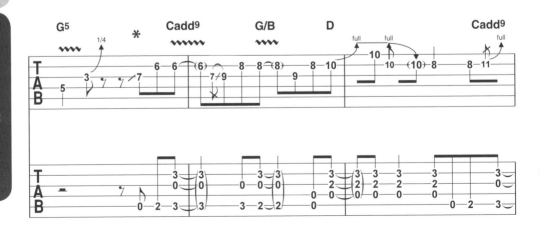

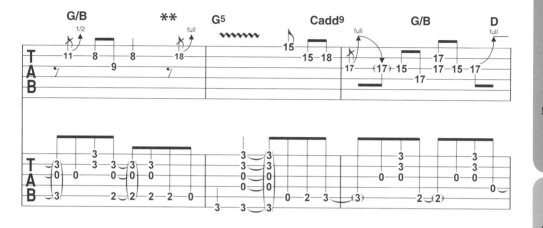

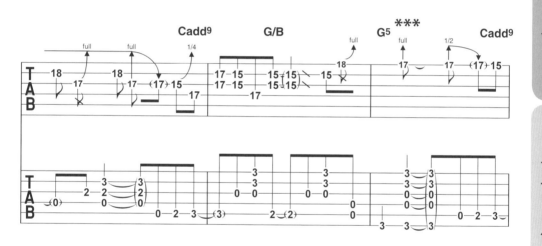

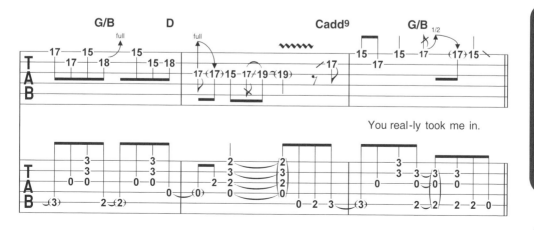

You real-ly took me in.

Beginner

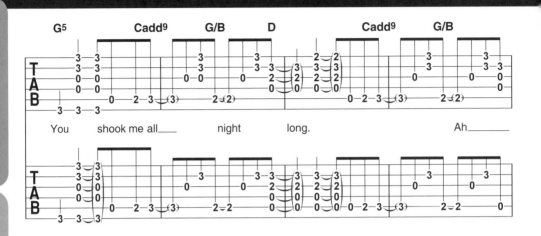

You   shook me all___   night   long.   Ah_____

Intermediate

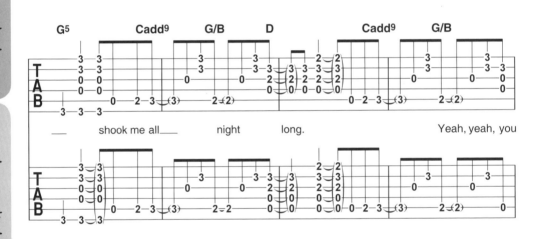

___   shook me all___   night   long.   Yeah, yeah, you

Intermediate +

TAB

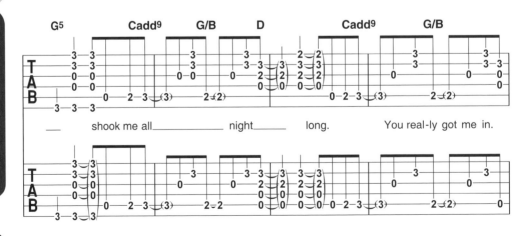

___   shook me all_____   night_____   long.   You real-ly got me in.

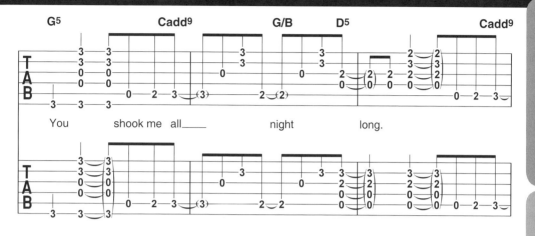

You shook me all____ night long.

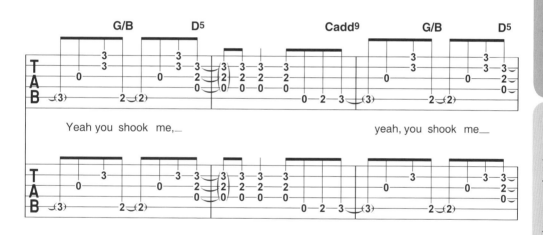

Yeah you shook me,_ yeah, you shook me_

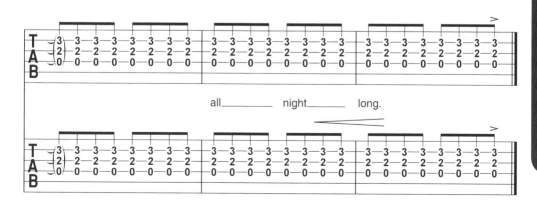

all_____ night_____ long.

229

Black Betty

Words & Music by Huddie Ledbetter

Intro
(Tempo 1)

| N.C. | | N.C. A5 | B5 | A5 | B5 | D5 | D5 A5 |

‖: B5 D E D A5 :‖ *Play x4*

| B5 | E | B5 | D | B5 | E | B5 | D |

| B5 | | B5 | | B | | B | |

Verse 1

  (Bm7)   **N.C.**
Whoa, Black Betty, (bam-ba-lam)
Whoa, Black Betty, (bam-ba-lam)

              (Bm7)
Black Betty had a child,   (bam-ba-lam)

              (Bm7)
The damn thing gone wild,   (bam-ba-lam)

                 (B5)
She said 'I'm worryin' outta mind.' (bam-ba-lam)

             (Bm7)
The damn thing gone blind. (bam-ba-lam)

          (Bm7)
I said Oh, Black Betty,   (bam-ba-lam)

             (Bm7)   **A5**
Whoa, Black Betty.   (bam-ba-lam)

Instr.

| B5 | A5 | B5 | D | D | A5 | ‖: B5 D E D A5 :‖ *Play x4*

| B5 | E | B5 | D | B5 | E | B5 | D | B5 | |

Verse 2

Oh, Black Betty, (bam-ba-lam)
Whoa, Black Betty, (bam-ba-lam)
She really gets me high, (bam-ba-lam)
You know that's no lie. (bam-ba-lam)
She's so rock steady, (bam-ba-lam)
And she's always ready. (bam-ba-lam)
Whoa, Black Betty, (bam-ba-lam)
Whoa, Black Betty. (bam-ba-lam)

Bridge 1
(Tempo 2)

Play **riff (x2)** | —— 2 —— |

Play **riff** | —— 2 —— |

Play **riff**

© COPYRIGHT 1963 FOLKWAYS MUSIC PUBLISHERS INCORPORATED.
KENSINGTON MUSIC LIMITED.
ALL RIGHTS RESERVED. INTERNATIONAL COPYRIGHT SECURED.

Solo |(B5) |(B5) |(B5) |(B5) $\frac{6}{4}$| (B5) $\frac{4}{4}$|

$\|$: D |D |D |D |
  |G |G |D |D |
  |B |B |B |B :$\|$

$\|$: D |D |D |D |
  |B |B |B |B :$\|$ *Play x3*

Bridge 2
(Tempo 1)

|B A |B A D |B A |A D |
|B A |B A D |B A |A A# |

Bridge 3
(Tempo 2)

|——2——| Play **riff 1** |——2——| Play **riff 1**

|(B5) |(B5) |(B5) |$\frac{6}{4}$ (B5) |$\frac{4}{4}$

(Tempo 1)

|B |B |

Verse 3

Whoa, Black Betty, (bam-ba-lam)
Whoa, Black Betty, (bam-ba-lam)
She's from Birmingham, (bam-ba-lam)
Way down in Alabam'. (bam-ba-lam)
Well, she's shakin' that thing, (bam-ba-lam)
Boy, she makes me sing. (bam-ba-lam)
Whoa, Black Betty, (bam-ba-lam)
Whoa, Black Betty. (BAM-BA-LAM)

Tempo Changes

This song includes sections played at very different speeds: we start at 116bpm (marked on the chord chart above as 'Tempo 1') but then switch to a brisk 250bpm for Bridge 1, the Solo section and Bridge 3 (marked on the chord chard as Tempo 2).

continued...

Introduction

This is Ram Jam's fantastic, psychedelic cover of an obscure Leadbelly song. There are so many cool guitar riffs licks and lines in here, and the whole song will sound best if you can perform it with 2 guitars (as on the record), either with a band, jam buddy, a 'looper' or through home recording…or of course by jamming along with the track.

Intro – Guitar 1

While there's some great riffing here, the most important things to think about are the rhythm and the groove, so do a lot of concentrated listening before you start playing the intro. In this section the biggest technical challenge is muting all the strings that you don't want to ring out, which when combined with some muted percussive hits means that your muting needs to be spot on.

To get the rhythm solid, you will need to start by playing slowly, making sure you have the rhythm right before speeding up. Don't be afraid to write out the count and count along if it helps.

The strumming follows the same principles that we've used in other sixteenth-note strumming work—anything on the beat or on a '+' will be played with a down-strum, and anything on the 'e' or 'a' will take an up-strum. There is a lot more information on this topic in the rhythm guitar lessons as part of the Intermediate Foundation lessons on the website.

Power chords are played as usual, and I'd recommend using finger 1 to play a small barre on fret 7 and finger 3 playing a small barre on fret 9—this should help you with your muting as well.

Intro - Guitar 2

Although the lead guitar part in the intro has a few tricky sections, I imagine the hardest part for most people will be getting the rhythm solid. Again, don't be afraid to write out the rhythms and count along. You should play along with the original recording at 50% speed (you can use software to slow the song down) for a while and get the timing of opening section and feel how it interacts with Guitar 1. A lot of the excitement in this tune comes from the interplay between the two guitars.

Use whatever picking you feel comfortable with, but a solid starting point would be to use alternate picking (as in the down and ups you would use if you were using sixteenth-note strumming to play the notes—down-picks on the beat and '+'s and up-picks on the 'e's and 'a's in between.

The fretting hand fingering should be fairly obvious, as it's playing mostly pentatonic-based licks, but playing out of the chords too. The one sticky bit you might come up against is the 10/11 slide where you will use finger 1, right after it's just played the 12th fret, so it's a bit of jump. You can see this being done in the music video of the song, so while it's tricky, it's authentic. Saying that, if you can find a fingering that suits you better, use it!

Watch out for the reverse bends—they are tricky to get sounding like the recording, but just keep practising them and listening. Play along with the record and try to copy it identically. It's great practice, and the better you get at emulating other people's playing, the better you will be able to express yourself, as you will be learning all about control.

Beginner

Intermediate

Intermediate +

TAB

 ## Verse

For the verses, the two guitars come together to play some cool Bm7 chords—the big deal again is the rhythm (the 'chord stab' comes on the '+' after 2) so keep it tight as a drum! Both parts must play exactly together and only hold the chord for a short time—don't be afraid to count it!

At the end of the verse, both guitars reprise the parts they played during the intro. On the repeat of this, they go into a new section—Bridge 1. Watch out for the 3/4 bar at the end, which a real killer and will throw your rhythm out if you are not solidly tapping your foot along!

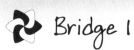 ## Bridge 1

Now we have some impressively tricky rhythm work! Aside from the 3/4 bar at the end of the last section (just to throw a spanner in the works!), we get an offbeat sixteenth-note pattern to go into! Sections like this are tricky to learn but once you get your head round it, it'll be easy enough to learn. The trick (as usual) is to take it slow and easy, so play along at 50% speed and get used to how the offbeat rhythms feel. Remember that if you are tapping your foot correctly (on the beat), then all of the chords will be between your foot taps until the double-stopped (fret) 7's on beat 4! It's hard, but if you take it slow, you will get it.

The two things that will help the most are listening and understanding. You can learn hard passages like this by using either one, but using both will be optimal. Listen a lot so that you know what the guitar part sounds like. Understand all the rhythms, both in terms of theory, and by what they feel like. Do both and it will be a load easier!

Solo - Guitar 1

After Bridge 1 the guitar divides into harmony parts, with Guitar 1 taking the lower harmony. The end section and the time signature change make it a little sticky but it's not too much of a challenge.

After the harmony line it goes into regular rhythm guitar, we've written out a 'guestimate' of the rhythm part, but (in this instance) you should just groove along with the band and not be too fussed about playing it exactly as the recording.

Watch out for the little ending tag where it breaks into triplets for a couple of beats, which can be tricky to navigate!

 ## Solo Guitar 2

Guitar 2 takes the higher harmony line after Bridge 1 and then cranks into a big solo. There are lots of nice licks to learn if you choose to, or you might like to improvise your own solo! It's pretty free which makes it hard to learn as a set piece, although it's a rewarding challenge if you decide to take it up. Personally I tend to crop licks from this kind of solo rather than learn it all, but it's your call.

Like with Guitar 1, you have the ending tag to deal with, and if you are playing in a band, you should strive to make the rhythm of the two guitar parts absolutely watertight!

Beginner

Intermediate

Intermediate +

TAB

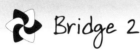 ## Bridge 2

Both guitars go into a complex harmony sequence. Again, getting the rhythm right will help you nail it, so playing along slowly is the key.

With a complex guitar part like this, the trick (if you can call it that) is to try to memorise the shapes of the parts, where the repeats are and how they relate to each other. It's worth getting familiar with both parts so you can hear how the related part works with yours—this will help keep the guitars tight. Having said that, I would recommend really nailing one part before learning the other, or they might get a bit confusing!

D.S. al Coda and Outro

D.S. (Dal Segno, I call it 'Da Squiggle') means go 'back to the sign'. Here, the sign is found at the start of the verse—it looks this: 𝄋

Once you go back to D.S. you will play 'al Coda' which means 'until the Coda' which is the symbol that looks like a gun sight! Like this: ⊕
Once you reach that you will jump to the end of the music where you'll see the sign and it says 'Coda' and you'll play from there until the end.

The last bit, the Outro, is a relatively simple part, with one guitar strumming frantically, and one playing a lead line, and ending in a big hit.

Job done! I hope you enjoyed this awesome and challenging tune!

Black Betty

Words & Music by Huddie Ledbetter

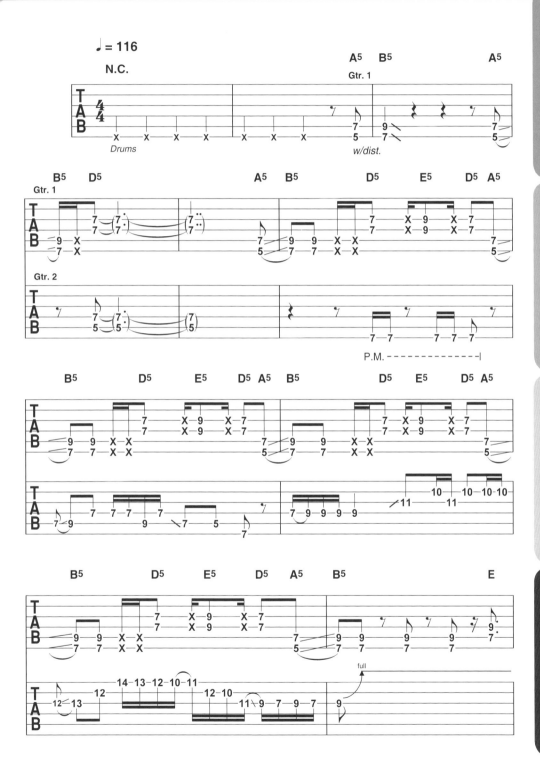

Beginner

Intermediate

Intermediate +

TAB

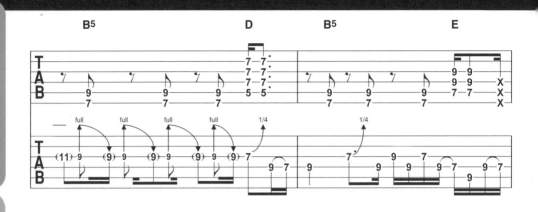

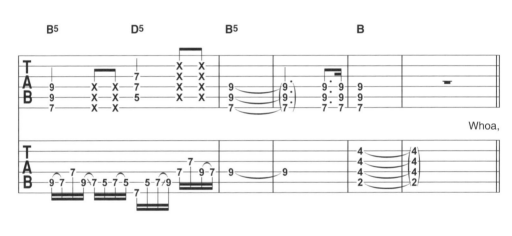

Whoa,

 Verse

Bm7

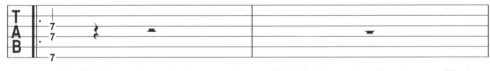

___ Black Bet-ty,	bam-ba-lam,	whoa,___ Black Bet-ty,	bam-ba-lam.___ Black
___ Black Bet-ty,	bam-ba-lam,	whoa,___ Black Bet-ty,	bam-ba-lam.___ She real-ly
___ Black Bet-ty,	bam-ba-lam,	whoa,___ Black Bet-ty,	bam-ba-lam.___ She's

Gtrs. 1+2   Bm7   Bm7

Bet-ty had   a   child,   bam-ba-lam, the damn   thing   gone wild,   bam-ba-lam. She said I'm
gets   me   high,   bam-ba-lam, you know   that's   no   lie,   bam-ba-lam.   She's
from   Birm ing ham,   bam-ba-lam, way   down_ in   A - labam',   bam-ba-lam. Well she's

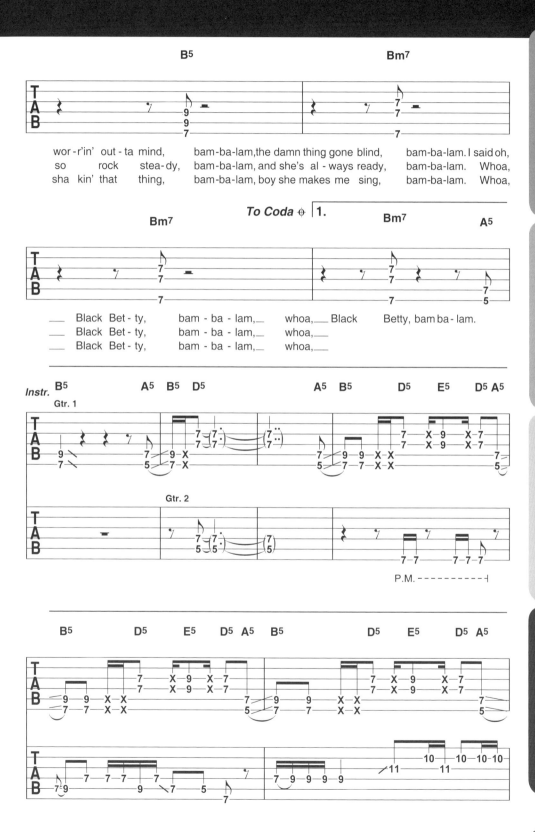

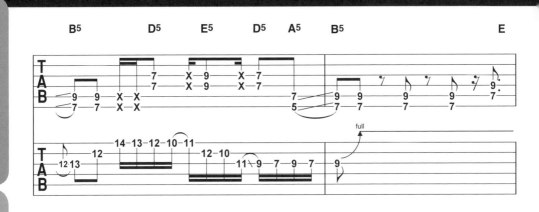

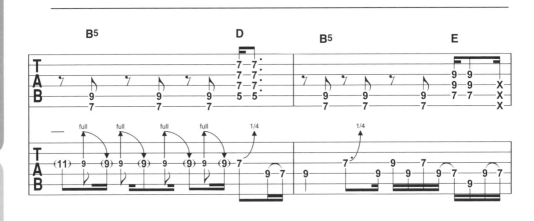

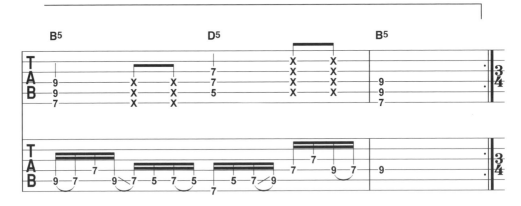

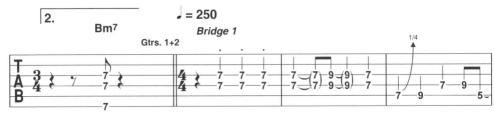

Black   Bet- ty,   bam- ba lam.

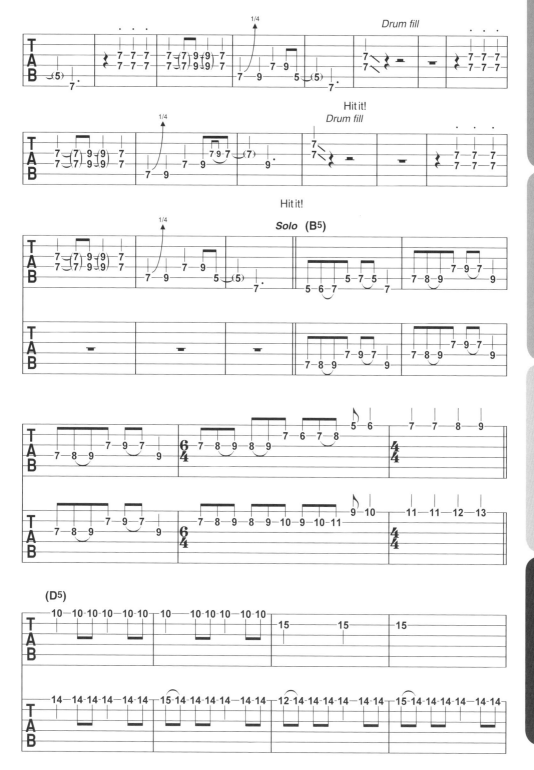

Black Betty (cont.)

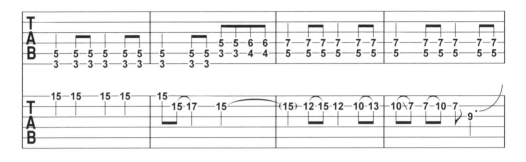

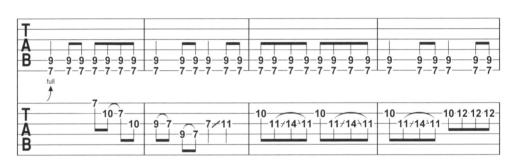

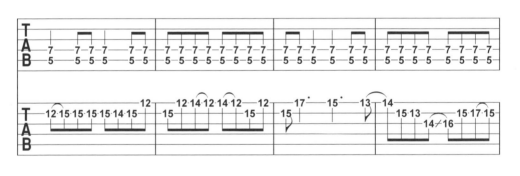

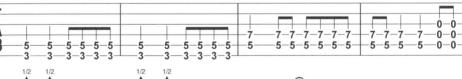

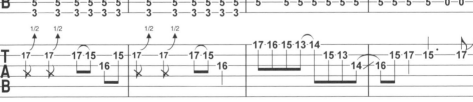

242

B5

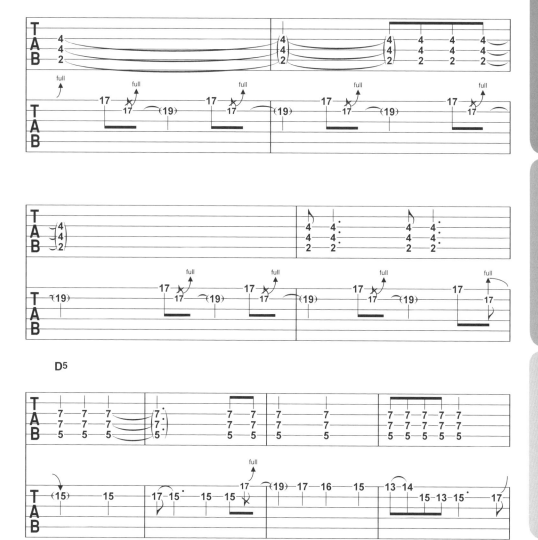

D5

B5

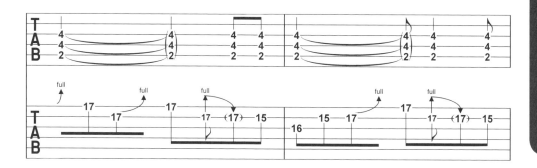

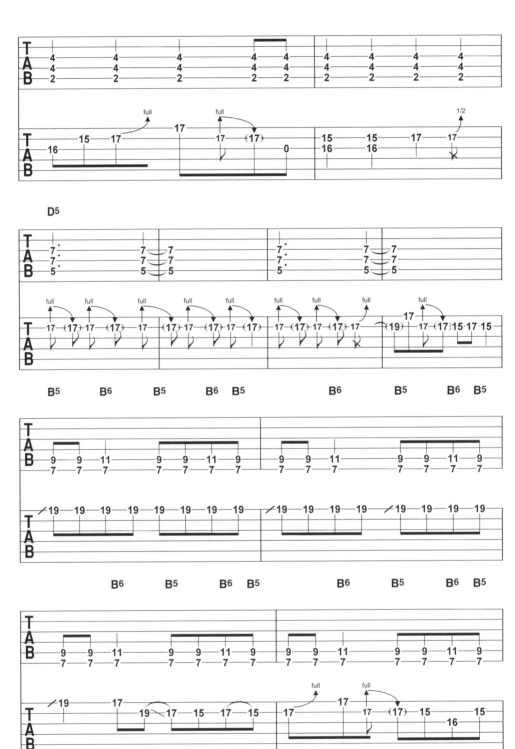

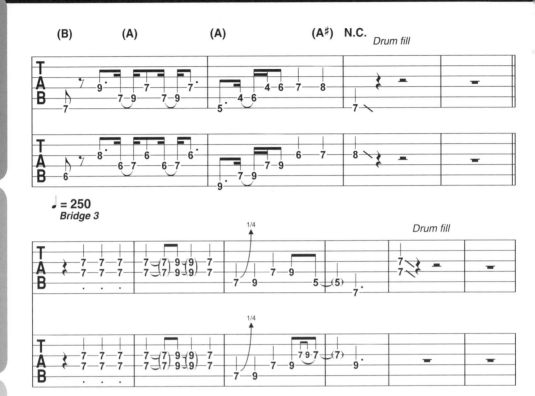

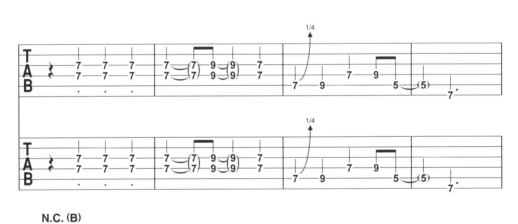

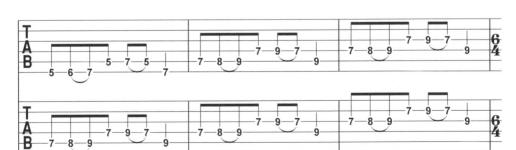

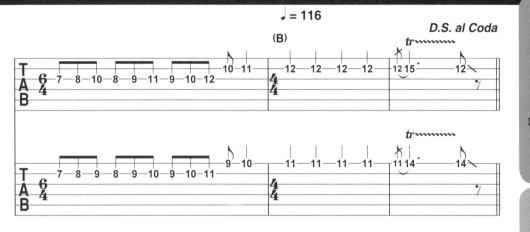

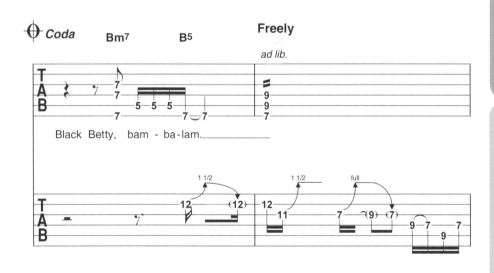

Black Betty, bam - ba-lam.

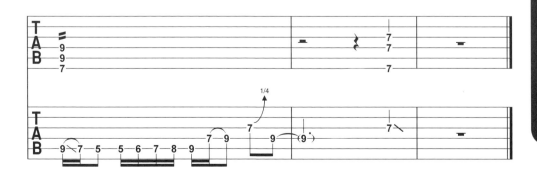

Justinguitar.com
Collect the series...

**Justinguitar.com
Beginner's Course
AM1001440**

**Justinguitar.com
Beginner's Songbook
AM1005334**

**Justinguitar.com
Vintage Songbook
AM1006214**

**Justinguitar.com
Pop Songbook
AM1005158**

**Justinguitar.com
Acoustic Songbook
AM1005147R**

**Justinguitar.com
Australian Songbook
AM1005191**

- Refresh your beginner skills with the comprehensive *Justinguitar.com Beginner's Course* and the accompanying *Beginner's Songbook.*

- Collect the other songbooks in the series. In each of the Pop, Vintage, Acoustic and Australian songbooks, you'll find 50 more songs specially chosen for guitarists who are looking to progress beyond beginner level.